Managing H and Social Care

A guide for supervisors and managers

Terry Smyth, MA, BA, RGN, RMN, DipN, RNT

Head of School of Health and Social Studies, Colchester Institute

For Lalitha, Amanda and Juliette

First published 1996 by
MACMILLAN PRESS LTD
Houndmills, Basingstoke, Hampshire RG21 6XS
and London
Companies and representatives
throughout the world

ISBN 0–333–60656–6

A catalogue record for this book is available
from the British Library

10 9 8 7 6 5 4 3 2
05 04 03 02 01 00 99 98

Typeset by Tek Art, Croydon, Surrey
Printed in Hong Kong

Contents

Acknowledgements

The author would like to thank those who have helped at various stages in the preparation of this book, in particular Jim Clarke, John Hawthorn, David Parry, Michael Key, Margaret Tomalin, Stuart Sillars, June Hawkins and Jan Kermeen.

The author and publishers wish to thank the following for permission to use copyright material: Hector Breeze for the cartoon on page 82; *Community Care* for the cartoons on pages 4, 11, 94 and 139; Photofusion for the photographs on pages 15, 118 and 123; Quantum Care for the photographs on pages 8, 21, 37, 41, 63, 75, 110, 112, 122, 125 and 130; and Malcolm Willett for the cartoons on pages 3, 27, 36, 48, 50, 84, 94, 96, 119, 124 and 126, which were first published in *Care Weekly*. The photographs on page 47 were supplied by the following: The multimedia personal computer by Mesh Computers Ltd and Trevor Peters Design; the handheld computer by Psion PLC; and the notebook computer by Tadpole Technology PLC.

Every effort has been made to trace all copyright holders, but if any have been inadvertently overlooked the publishers will be pleased to make the necessary arrangements at the first opportunity.

1 About this book

Managing in the care field is particularly complex and difficult because it is about meeting the needs of vulnerable people. I have written this book from personal experience and from many years of observing and teaching managers who are trying to achieve excellence in circumstances which are often uncertain or unclear. I have used the Management Standards developed by the Management Charter Initiative (MCI) to ensure that the book reflects current thinking.

Managing in the care sector is special because all care workers and care managers share core values and philosophies. Although each caring occupation and profession has its own unique approach to care work, there are common and fundamental beliefs which unite all care workers – such as respect for the individual, the value of cultural diversity to society and a commitment to justice and equality.

1.1 Who is this book for?

I have based this book on the real experiences of supervisory managers working in a wide range of care fields. You will find the book valuable if you are:

- working in the care sector at a supervisory management level, or hoping to move into a management role in the future. For example, you might be: a manager or supervisor in residential, day or home care; a supervisor in a playgroup or nursery; a qualified health or social care professional, perhaps a nurse, social worker, occupational therapist or physiotherapist, with team management responsibilities.
- following an educational programme, such as: NVQ/SVQ (National Vocational Qualifications/Scottish Vocational Qualifications) in management, based on the MCI Management Standards; City and Guilds Foundation Management for Care or Advanced Management for Care; BTEC (Business and Technology Education Council) Certificate in Management Studies; LGMB (Local Government Management Board) Diploma in the Management of Care Services; courses validated by the NEBS Management (National Examinations Board for Supervision and Management).

1.2 Aims of the book

The book aims to give you:

- an introduction to the management of health and social care;
- underpinning knowledge for NVQ/SVQs in management at the supervisory level;
- ideas and encouragement, including how to become more reflective and creative in your work.

The book is not intended to make you an expert in every aspect of management work. For example, the book does not cover all the relevant legislation in any detail; you will need to refer to specialist sources in these cases. I have included references to some of these in the suggestions for further reading in the relevant chapters.

1.3 Structure of the book

There are ten chapters covering the key areas of managing in a care context – quality, resources, managing people, organising work, communication and dealing with change.

Each chapter includes a range of activities and examples applying the theory to practice. Ideas for further reading are also included so that you can follow up areas that interest you.

1.4 How to use the book

How you use this book will depend on your individual needs. You can use it to refer to as and when you need guidance on a particular area of your work or studies. You may want to work through it chapter by chapter to get an overall idea of a manager's job. If you are following a course in management, your tutor might refer you to particular chapters, sections and activities. If particular issues crop up in your work or studies, you can turn easily to the appropriate chapter by referring to the detailed contents list or the index.

All chapters contain 'Activities'. They encourage you to think about practical problems and issues in a 'reflective' way. They usually have no right or wrong answers, but are there to help you think about problems. Generally, a book is only as good as its ability to make its readers think. The idea of reflective practice is described in Chapter 3.

You do not have to undertake any of the activities at the precise point in the text where they are introduced. As a student, I was always very wary of books that said 'stop now and do so and so…' Most of us don't work like that. Use this book in the way that suits you, and that applies to the suggested activities as well as the text.

If you are a practising manager in the care sector, or if your course includes work placements, you can make use of your first-hand practical experience. You should try to develop your reflective and problem-solving skills by learning from your everyday experience.

You will find that learning is quicker if you have the help of a mentor in your work place or placement. Many organisations will provide mentors for staff undertaking courses and for students on placement.

You will also find it helpful to pair up with a colleague who is also interested in developing his or her managerial skills – you will gain more from the many activities in the book if you can share your thoughts.

If you wish to use this book to work towards a management NVQ/SVQ, you will be able to find out more from your employer, from educational institutions, such as colleges of further education, or from your local TEC (Training and Enterprise Council). Colleges will also be able to tell you about other management training opportunities in your area.

Most chapters also include suggestions for further reading. Use these references when you need to follow up a topic in greater detail. You should also make sure that you are very familiar with your own organisation's policies and procedures. These will help you to see how employers interpret many of the general principles and legal requirements in care work.

1.5 Terms used

In the care sector, labels can be controversial. For the majority of this book, I have decided to use the generic term 'manager'. 'Supervisory manager' is too cumbersome to use repeatedly and the term 'supervisor' can be muddled with a person offering professional supervision – see Chapter 10.

I shall use the term 'team', 'team member(s)' or 'staff' when writing about those for whom managers are responsible.

Over the years, the 'user of the service' has been referred to in many different ways – client, patient, customer, user, resident. However, I believe that the term 'client' has become the most useful generic term because it can be used in both health and social services without too much difficulty. In addition, it conveys many of those desirable values that are to do with 'service', without taking away the 'customer' dimension.

2 What is supervisory management?

If you are a supervisory manager, you have taken the first step on the management ladder. In most cases, you will be formally accountable to middle or senior managers. What determines whether or not you are a 'supervisory manager' is the range of roles you carry out and the amount of responsibility you are given. However, if you work in a small independent care organisation, such as a nursery or small residential home, your job may include aspects of supervisory manager, middle manager and proprietor! Even in large organisations, there can be a great deal of blurring between roles and levels. Although you may not be in complete control of the end result of your work, your contribution will be vital to the success of the organisation.

Job titles for those people with supervisory management responsibilities are very varied. Sometimes traditional titles are used which emphasise the professional background of the post holder. In other cases, the titles are more descriptive. In the jobs listed here as examples, post holders are expected to operate at the supervisory level as far as their management responsibilities are concerned.

The health sector

Occupational Therapy
Head IV Occupational Therapist
Senior I Occupational Therapist

Physiotherapy
Senior I Physiotherapist
Superintendent IV Physiotherapist

Nursing
Senior Staff Nurse
Sister or Charge Nurse
Ward Manager
Clinical Leader
Project Manager

Child Care
Nursery Manager
Officer-in-Charge
Deputy Manager

Social Care
Care Manager
Resource Centre Manager
Unit Manager
Officer-in-Charge
Assistant Principal

Whatever your job title, your relationship with your team is critical because you will be working very closely together. In contrast to more senior managers, you will plan your work over the short to medium term, and will be responsible for a small group of staff and the material resources needed to carry out your tasks.

2.1 Supervisory management and professional supervision

The term 'supervision' is used in different ways in different professional contexts, especially in the fields of health and social care. There are two main interpretations:

- '*management supervision*' – concerned with the achievement of results;
- '*professional supervision*' – concerned with professional support and development.

Supervision in the management sense is what this book is mainly about. It covers a broad range of skills, not all of which are concerned directly with people. For example, you need to know about money and material resources. However, supervision in the professional development sense is an integral part of the role of many managers and is covered in Chapter 10.

Some of you may receive regular professional supervision as part of your everyday work. For others, the idea may be completely new. This book takes the view that a well-organised professional supervision system is an important foundation for effective and efficient health and social care.

2.2 The structure of organisations

The diagram below shows a line management structure with each supervisory manager accountable to a particular middle manager and responsible for a staff team. Each part of the organisation has a specific function and staff at each level have defined roles and follow rules and procedures. This kind of organisation is often described as bureaucratic.

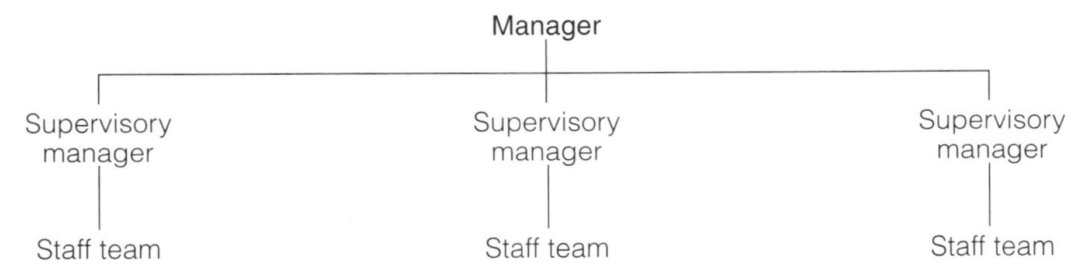

Charles Handy has likened this arrangement to a Greek temple (see diagram below) where the pillars are the specific functions of the organisation that are coordinated by a narrow band of senior managers (Handy 1993). As Handy points out, a bureaucratic organisation works very well when conditions are stable but has trouble 'when the ground shakes'. In other words, when external conditions change, bureaucracies cannot adapt easily or quickly.

The ground has shaken quite noticeably in the care sector in recent years. The tremors have led many people to look for more flexible organisations which are capable of responding rapidly to major upheavals in government policy and legislation. Major changes in community care for older people, for example, have required care organisations to re-think their aims and range of services.

For these reasons, the classic bureaucracy has often given way to organisational structures which place more emphasis on team work, autonomy and concern for the needs of customers. Rigid departments are replaced by staff groups and networks which can communicate more easily across the organisation. The end result is often described as a *matrix*.

In a matrix, members of staff may be responsible to different managers for different aspects of their job. A matrix needs staff who can tolerate some uncertainty since, from time to time, they will wonder who their boss is!

The diagram opposite shows a simple matrix. You will see that it looks very different from a conventional line management diagram. Three examples will illustrate how the matrix works:

- The day care manager controls a team of staff whose job is to meet the needs of the day care clients. However, the Personnel Department is responsible for organising the recruitment of new staff to the day care team; the manager will play a big part in who gets appointed, of course, but is not responsible for the process.
- The job of the Enterprise Department is to discover new ways of providing care and increasing income. To get a new project off the ground,

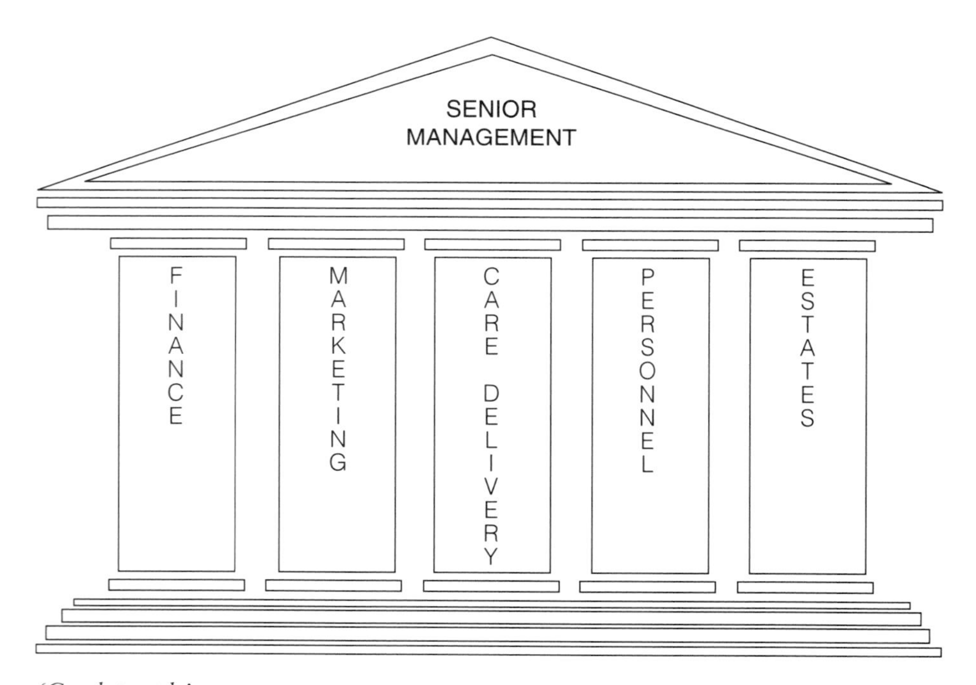

'Greek temple'

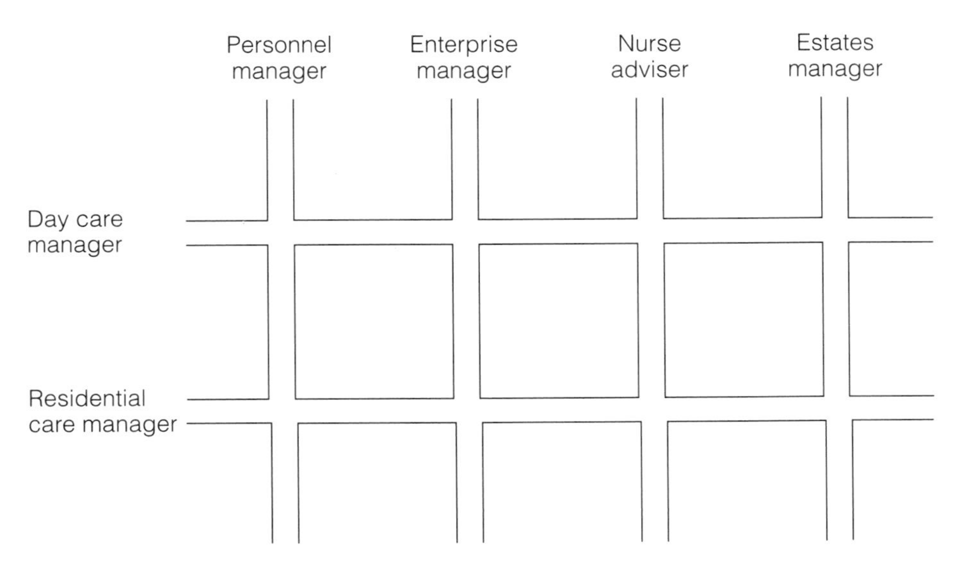

NB staff on both axes will be accountable to senior management, for example both the day care manager and the personnel manager may be accountable to the same senior manager (not shown on the diagram).

Matrix structure

a *project manager* from the Enterprise Department negotiates with all other departments to identify members of their staff who can form a *project team*. These members of staff will be released for part of their working week for the duration of the project. The costs of covering absent staff will be met through the income generated by the Enterprise Department.

- Both day services and residential services need professional nursing input. One of the senior nurses would be identified as being responsible for offering professional nursing advice (the *nursing adviser*) across the whole organisation. However, unless the organisation is quite large, she or he might also have a line management role in, say, the day services.

In each example, the barriers between departments are broken down. Each becomes increasingly aware of the others' concerns and priorities, and can work better to achieve the goals of the whole organisation.

Organisational structures need to be compatible with the culture of the organisation. Insistence on a rigid bureaucracy in an organisation whose culture values, team work and blurring of roles may cause problems. In health and social care, there are often clashes of this type, in particular between the approach of the organisation as a whole and the culture of each of the professional groups which contribute to it.

Large health and social care organisations, such as NHS Trusts and social service departments, have to maintain a balance between these different, sometimes competing, interest groups. With the best will in the world, it is unlikely that there will ever be total agreement between doctors, nurses, social workers, occupational therapists, health care assistants, administrators and clients/potential clients.

Because of this rich diversity of cultures, we find that organisational structures in health and social care often contain elements of both line and matrix structures. This is both their strength and their weakness: on the one hand, they can be dynamic organisations which show rapid change and renewal, avoiding fossilisation; on the other, they can be so changeable that they create an insecure working environment for their staff.

2.3 Roles and functions

All managers in care settings undertake a number of key roles. These include:

- *leader* – of a team; a function which involves the abilities to direct, listen, collaborate and motivate;
- *carer* – for clients, staff and themselves;
- *adviser/teacher* – to team members and often to peers;
- *communicator* – all supervisory activities demand effective communication;
- *intermediary* – the complex task of acting both as a filter for decisions coming from elsewhere in the organisation (often from above) and as a representative or advocate for team members;
- role model – demonstrating the skills of management to those team members who aspire to promotion.

Through these various roles, supervisors carry out a range of complex functions, including:

- improving quality;
- planning, monitoring and controlling;
- contributing to staff recruitment, staff development and training;
- organising and evaluating work;
- creating, maintaining and enhancing good working relationships;
- handling information and communicating well.

> **ACTIVITY**
>
> Look again at the lists of roles and functions in this chapter. Consider each in turn and assess how well you carry them out.
>
> Make a note of how you would like to improve your present skills.

Leader, carer, communicator

2.4 Being a supervisory manager

Taking on the extra responsibility of management is never easy. There will be many times when you wish you hadn't! Perhaps you had little choice. Often a professional training, such as social work, occupational therapy or nursing, brings with it an expectation of management. Certainly, courses leading to this kind of qualification contain an introduction to management. Despite this, no preparation can ever adequately cover the rich array of challenges you will face. For example:

- you will not always be popular with your team;
- work will not always go well and you may not know how to solve every problem;
- you may feel that your own manager puts too much pressure on you.

In the midst of all this, your relationship with your team is critical: at one and the same time, the most satisfying and the most stressful aspect of the job. Middle and top managers are sometimes able to make decisions and then leave others – perhaps you – to deal with the consequences. On the one hand, when work is going well, you will feel part of the success in a way that can never be experienced by those further away in the organisational hierarchy. On the other hand, you are likely to share all the disappointments as they occur.

2.5 Personal qualities

It would be unrealistic to try to list the qualities of an ideal manager: no one would be able to live up to them all and it would be equally impossible to say which could be left out. So, what can usefully be said? A few personal observations might be helpful:

- Effective managers come in all shapes, sizes and personality types.
- Don't expect to succeed quickly in all aspects of your job or to win every argument. You cannot be right every time – although you should try! A healthy degree of humility is necessary whatever the level of management.
- Get to know your strengths and limitations; sometimes it can be better to take a back seat and let others take the lead.
- Be as fair as you can; the best way of achieving this is to be as open as possible about what's going on and the decisions you have to take.
- Be ready to see conflict as just part of the ebb and flow of your everyday working life and try not to take criticism personally.

KEY CONCEPTS

These definitions will help you to understand the rest of this book.

accountability Where the 'buck stops'. Responsibility and authority for actually carrying out a task may be delegated by a manager but he or she remains accountable for seeing that the task is completed.

authority The use of power in a legitimate way, for example through the position – such as 'manager'– that someone holds in an organisation.

autonomy The capacity to think, act, choose and make decisions freely and independently. Professional autonomy is guarded jealously by the care professions; in fact, a high degree of autonomy is often considered to be one of the signs of a profession.
control The process of knowing how well actions conform to plans. It involves setting standards, measuring performance and correcting any variations.
delegation Giving a member of your staff the responsibility and the authority to carry out a task.
evaluation Making a judgement as a result of information collected by the monitoring process.
monitoring Collecting information and using this to check performance; for monitoring to be effective, the information collected must be relevant and must reach the right people.
power The use of influence to bring about a desired result. Power stems from position and status, expertise, personality or physical force. Care workers only use physical force in extreme cases, for example where disturbed clients need restraint.
responsibility Implementing a task and accepting the consequences.

ACTIVITY

A disproportionate number of managers are men. Does this apply to your own workplace?

What is the balance between men and women in supervisory and other management jobs in your organisation?

What do you think about this? Discuss your thoughts with your colleagues.

ACTIVITY

Look back at the organisational structures described in this chapter. How far does your own organisation fit any one of these descriptions? Try to identify the features of a bureaucracy and those of a matrix. Remember there is no one right way of organising people to produce the best results. Most organisations in health and social care will show mixed features.

Reading on...

★ Catt, Stephen E. and Miller, Donald S. (1991) *Supervision: working with people*, Irwin, Boston.
★ Handy, Charles B. (1993), *Understanding Organisations*, Penguin Books, Harmondsworth.

3 Managing in a care context

As a manager, you will be more effective if you understand the social, political and professional contexts in which you work. You will then be better able to contribute to local policy, to anticipate developments and trends, and to exert more influence over your own working life. This process of empowerment will benefit you, your clients and your staff.

In much of your work, you will have to manage in situations of some uncertainty where there are no precise rules to follow. Under these conditions, you need to be able to learn effectively from experience. By using the skills of reflective practice, described later in this chapter, you will make good use of these situations and help to ensure that you and your staff are more able to provide sensitive, individualised and quality care to clients.

3.1 The current social and political context

All care providers have had to come to terms with major changes in recent years. Some of the most important are:

- the introduction of competition and market forces leading to the creation of a *mixed economy* in health and social care (i.e. care is provided by a combination of the public, private and voluntary sectors);
- the reorganisation of many services into two separate functions: *purchasers* and *providers* of care; health authorities and social service departments assess the health and social care needs of their local communities – they then *purchase* services to meet these needs;
- the need to demonstrate *value for money*;
- the growing emphasis on *standards of care* and *quality assurance*, and the need for clear statements about what the client is entitled to;
- the introduction of *charters* in the public sector; for example the Patient's Charter which describes what patients have the right to expect from the National Health Service.

Purchasers and providers

Markets need people who want to sell (*providers*) and those who want to buy (*purchasers*). This split between purchaser and provider has been most obvious in the NHS where the old District Health Authorities have been converted into purchasers of health care, and the hospitals and community health services have been restructured into NHS Trusts which provide the health care services. In social services, the picture is more complicated. Some social service departments have moved rapidly into arrangements similar to those in the NHS; others have continued to provide a full range of services themselves.

An important result of these changes is that local health and social service authorities have become *enablers*, i.e. they no longer provide all the various health and social services themselves – they 'buy them in' from a variety of providers, from the statutory, private or voluntary sectors. This contractual approach has stimulated the private and voluntary sectors to offer a wider range of services. For example, residential care and nursing homes are diversifying into day and home care.

However, a contractual approach might encourage short term arrangements. Providers of a service need some degree of stability, without which they cannot easily develop long term plans. Insecure conditions can lead to lower staff morale, difficulties in staff recruitment and longer term financial problems.

While the move towards greater competition may have many advantages, its impact on the lives of individual care workers may be much less favourable. Flexibility can imply short term contracts and job insecurity. Managers at all levels should try to bring the benefits of flexibility to clients without damaging the lives of care workers.

ACTIVITY

The division of the care sector into purchasers and providers has been a significant change in health and social care. Consider the following questions from your own point of view and that of your clients.

- Has the split between purchaser and provider influenced your area of work? If so, how?
- What are the effects on individual practitioners and managers of a more commercial approach to care?
- What differences, if any, have the changes made to your own attitude to your work, and that of your colleagues?
- Do these market arrangements suit all client groups equally, for example minority ethnic groups?

The Patient's Charter

Charters are being used in many areas of the public and private sectors, such as health and social services, colleges and universities, and commercial organisations like banks. They are a way of making clear what a customer's rights are and they set out standards of performance to be achieved by the organisation.

This chapter includes extracts from the original Patient's Charter as an example of a national charter relevant to care workers. The Department of Health distributed The Patient's Charter to all households, as part of the Government's Citizen's Charter initiative. As the document puts it: 'The Patient's Charter sets out clearly for the first time your rights to care in the National Health Service and the National and Local Charter Standards which the Government intends to see achieved.'

In all, there were ten *rights* set out. Seven of these were just confirming what had already been established; three were new.

Existing rights

1 To receive health care on the basis of clinical need, regardless of the ability to pay.
2 To be registered with a GP.
3 To receive emergency medical care at any time, through your GP or the emergency ambulance service and hospital accident and emergency departments.
4 To be referred to a consultant, acceptable to you, when your GP thinks it necessary, and to be referred for a second opinion if you and your GP agree this is desirable.
5 To be given a clear explanation of any treatment proposed, including any risks and any alternatives, before you decide whether you will agree to the treatment.
6 To have access to your health records, and to know that those working for the NHS are under a legal duty to keep their contents confidential.
7 To choose whether or not you wish to take part in medical research or medical student training.

> **ACTIVITY**
>
> Consider the following types of care activity. How much choice does the potential client have in each case?
>
> - residential care for older people;
> - a dental filling;
> - cosmetic surgery, for example a face-lift;
> - hip replacement operation;
> - occupational therapy;
> - places in day care nurseries.

New rights

Three new Rights came into effect from 1 April 1992:

8 To be given detailed information on local health services, including quality standards and maximum waiting times. [Since April 1992, local charters and standards leaflets have proliferated and can be found in GP surgery waiting rooms, hospitals and clinics.]

9 To be guaranteed admission for treatment by a specific date no later than two years from the day when your consultant places you on a waiting list. [Many health service managers have had major problems meeting the target. Critics have argued that this approach may have led to less urgent cases being brought forward unnecessarily simply to satisfy the Government's target.]

10 To have any complaint about NHS services – whoever provides them – investigated and to receive a full and prompt reply from the chief executive or general manager.

The Patient's Charter, like all others, is reviewed and updated regularly.

Although the introduction of a market implies customer choice, in health and social care few individuals can choose freely from the available services. To be able to do so would require considerable personal wealth. For example, within the NHS, most people have to rely on the local Health Authority to buy appropriate services on their behalf. In other cases, such as dental care, services are more within reach of the average person and many more patients are able to choose from a range of competing dentists.

Care in the community

Most current community care policies have been influenced by the care required by older people. This is inevitable because older people represent the largest single client group and so need most resources.

In 1986, the Audit Commission produced a report entitled *Making a Reality of Community Care*. It criticised the system of social security payments which, the report maintained, encouraged over-use of residential care. Keeping people in their own homes for longer, with support from community resources, would not only be better for the individual (the moral argument) but be cheaper too (the economic argument). The Audit Commission Report was followed by the 'Griffith's Report' (1988), the 'Wagner Report' (*Residential Care: a Positive Choice*, 1988) and the White Paper *Caring for People* (1989). These various publications and the debate which surrounded them culminated in the NHS and Community Care Act 1990.

Legislation

Many important pieces of legislation have been introduced in recent years which provide the statutory framework for the present approach to care:

The NHS and Community Care Act 1990 is a wide-ranging piece of legislation and has been followed by a number of policy guidance documents. Amongst other things, these:

- require local authorities to coordinate the arrangements for assessing community care needs. Local authorities consult widely with a variety of agencies, such as health, social services and the independent sector, and then produce a community care plan for their area;

- require local authorities to publish complaints procedures;
- expect local authorities to publish information about the types of services available in different sectors, the standards expected, and the referral, assessment and review procedures;
- set up independent inspection units to inspect residential homes in the statutory and independent sectors to the same standards.

The Children Act 1989 was implemented in 1991. The law embodies the principle that the prime concern of workers and authorities must be the welfare of children. All managers whose work brings them into contact with children as clients must become familiar with the areas of the Act which affect their work. You should ensure that you know how the Act might apply to your work. Amongst many other things, the Act includes:

- the registration and inspection of children's homes and day centres for children under the age of eight;
- the requirement for agencies to give due consideration to a child's race, religion, language, and culture.

The Race Relations Act 1976 makes it unlawful to discriminate on grounds of race. This covers four areas of possible discrimination:

- *direct discrimination* – for example, refusing to employ a person because he or she is black;
- *indirect discrimination* – for example, applying a condition which favours one group over another;
- *segregation* – for example, by insisting that all black children sit together for meals in a day nursery just because they are black;
- *victimisation* – for example, refusing to refer an Asian client with learning disabilities for speech therapy because his mother had earlier complained about the way staff spoke to her.

The Sex Discrimination Acts of 1975 and 1986 make it unlawful for an employer to discriminate on grounds of gender or marital status. Both women and men have equal protection under this legislation.

There are circumstances where the Race Relations Act and the Sex Discrimination Act do not apply. Sometimes membership of a particular racial group is a 'genuine occupational qualification' (GOQ) – for instance, if it is intended to provide care to a specific racial group, then to recruit a care worker of the same racial background might be permitted. Similarly, it could be legal for a woman to be recruited for a post in an establishment catering solely for women.

3.2 Managing in a care organisation

The changes described in this Chapter have led to a greater variety of jobs in the care sector. New roles and new job titles have been created. Two features are particularly important:

- emphasis on work in the community;
- inter-agency working, for instance collaboration between health and social care staff, or between the private and voluntary sectors.

As a result of these trends, you may find yourself responsible for a team which includes workers from different professions, such as social workers, occupational therapists, nurses and care assistants or support workers. If you manage a multidisciplinary team, you need to be aware of the different ways in which groups of staff see their roles. Make a special effort to learn about the how your colleagues see their roles and what they think about their work.

ACTIVITY

All managers link with a large number of other people in the course of their work – care professionals, administrators, relatives and so on. Just how many can come as a surprise. Draw a diagram showing these relationships – a 'role map' . Don't make this too complicated – the aim is to establish the key relationships and to get an impression of the variety involved. Put yourself in the middle of this 'map' and then place others as appropriate.

Here is an example prepared by a playgroup leader:

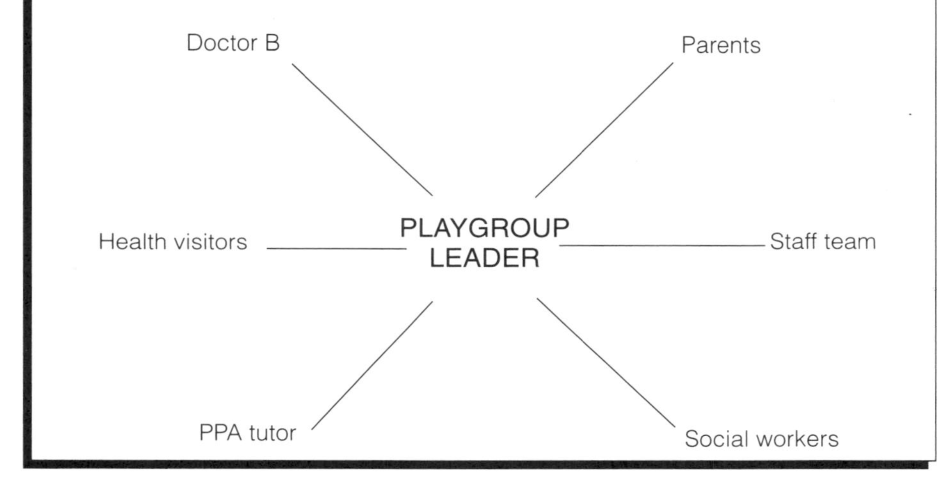

Family centre

Values in care management

Does being a manager in the care sector create role conflict? Are the values of care compatible with those of management? These issues can cause you considerable strain, especially where your job includes direct care for clients.

A great deal of interest has been shown by both health and social services in developing joint management training. One initiative has been the Management Education Scheme by Open Learning (MESOL) – coordinated by the NHS Training Directorate. The MESOL management framework sets out care values as follows:

- a commitment to anti-discriminatory practices;
- emphasising individual rights;
- promoting customer choice, dignity, privacy, fulfilment and independence;
- working towards justice and equity;
- delivering services that are sensitive to the rich tapestry of cultures in the communities served by the personal social services;
- delivering services geared to the needs of individuals.

As a care manager, you should try to work in ways which express these values.

Another view of care is that it is about 'allowing others to grow' (Mayeroff, 1990). Your caring approach as a manager should reveal itself according to how you allow both your clients and staff to grow and develop to their full potential.

ACTIVITY

If you manage or work in a multidisciplinary team, try to find out what colleagues feel about their jobs.

If this is to be the first discussion of its type, it might be a good idea to focus on a particular issue or problem and take it from there.

On the whole, colleagues will welcome this because it is an opportunity to share beliefs, values and practices and, by doing so, to achieve a greater understanding between groups.

ACTIVITY

Look through the values listed in this section.

- Do you support them all?
- Which are most difficult to achieve within your organisation? Why do you think this is?
- Do you find any conflict between these values and your role as a manager?

3.3 Reflective practice

Procedures, policies and guidelines are essential to the smooth running of any organisation but they are not enough. The missing ingredient is the ability to learn from experience and, as a result of this, to change and develop your practice.

Reflective practice is a concept that has emerged in the past few years to explain this process of learning from experience. In what is now a well known book called *The Reflective Practitioner*, Donald Schön set out his ideas about how professionals think while doing their job (he called this 'reflection-in-action'). Schön distinguished between the kind of knowledge gained through traditional study – books, school, university – and that acquired through work experiences. His ideas have subsequently been applied to a very wide range of different occupations, from management to music, architecture to nursing, and engineering to social work. This breadth of application is one of the strengths of Schön's theories.

Schön's main ideas are as follows:

- Most professional work takes place under conditions of considerable 'uncertainty, instability, uniqueness, and value conflict'.

- Some problems can be solved through the use of established knowledge and techniques; others are much more untidy yet often extremely important. As Schön graphically put it 'in the swamp are the problems of greatest human concern'.
- Professional activity is an art as well as a science. You will not be able to solve many of your problems by using procedures or rules. In these cases, you will have to think on your feet and improvise solutions – you will have to use your 'professional artistry'.

Using your intuition

Sometimes you make judgements based on your *gut feelings*. Schön calls this 'knowing-in-action'. Everyday experience will tell you that this approach can work. Success lies in the degree to which we can link our past experiences with the present problem. However, you will also know that intuition can be fallible.

'Reflection-in-action'

Quite often, your usual ways of getting to grips with problems fail to work. Intuition breaks down and made-to-measure solutions are unavailable. In cases like these, you are forced to pause for thought. You may say to yourself, 'This seems rather puzzling, what's going on here?'

You may also be startled by an unexpected success. You did not expect things to work so well and you ask yourself the question, 'What did I really do here?'

Both situations are examples of one of Schön's key ideas, 'reflection-in-action', which refers to the ability to think and learn while doing.

Encouraging reflective practice

Reflective practice gives you the chance to become a more competent manager, but the implications can be far-reaching. The more you encourage

ACTIVITY

Think about the kinds of problems you have to deal with every day. How many of them can you solve by simply using a piece of textbook knowledge or a procedure straight from the manual? You may have come across some easy ones but it is likely that most will be characterised by 'uncertainty, instability, uniqueness and value conflict'.

For example:

1 You are in charge of a shift in a residential home for older people when you learn that Mrs Heinmann has wandered out into the snow in her night-dress. You ask a care assistant to fetch her back quickly but he asks you what he should do if she refuses and, if necessary, should he lie by telling her that her son has come to visit. How do you weigh up the risk of hypothermia against the damage done by lying to the client? The answer won't be found in a textbook.

2 As a home help organiser, you are always being called upon to arrange assistance without adequate numbers of staff. You believe that, for some clients, the situation has reached breaking point. Departmental reorganisation is on the cards in the next month or two. Would a complaint now jeopardise your chances of securing your job in the future?

your staff to become aware of what they are doing, the more you are promoting thoughtful and sensitive care.

By encouraging reflective practice, you will be developing colleagues who are better able to anticipate client needs and are prepared to share and negotiate with clients. However, you won't always find it easy or comfortable. Some staff may surprise you with new suggestions. You may not agree with them all and, given a more open, thinking climate, you will not be able to fall back on the authority of your position.

Try to handle these conflicts of ideas as they occur. Sometimes this clash will overflow into a conflict between the people involved as well as between ideas. Recognise this as a possibility and discuss it with your staff at an early stage. The effort you put in to developing a culture of reflective practice is worthwhile because you will be raising the quality of professional practice in your area of work and raising staff morale.

Reading on...

⋆ Community Care Series on Purchasing: 28 October 1993 to 16/23 December 1993 (No. 990 to 997). This series of seven articles covers a number of controversial issues of concern to many supervisory managers.

⋆ Mayeroff, Milton (1990) *On Caring*, Harper Perennial, New York. A beautiful little book that will delight anyone who wants a short, well written and engaging view of caring.

⋆ Schön, Donald A. (1991) *The Reflective Practitioner*, Avebury, Aldershot.

⋆ Stark, Michael (1991) *Not for profit, not for sale*, Policy Journals in Association with the Chartered Institute of Management Accountants. This is a well written summary of the policies which were developed through the 1980s and how managers should make a contribution to developments in the public services.

Try describing a diagram using words only

- *To express emotions and attitudes.* Obvious examples are smiles or laughter, sneers or dismissive gestures. More subtly, some people express their lack of respect, or perhaps embarrassment, by refusing to make eye-contact – for example the nurse who finds it difficult to tell a relative bad news. Some people are inclined to reduce eye contact in the presence of a superior and this should not be taken as lack of attention or interest.
- *To emphasise or contradict what we say.* A serious point may be accompanied by a firm, steady gaze. On the other hand, someone who is trying hard to lie may possibly indicate unease by restless hand movements or a reluctance to make eye-contact. There are no infallible methods in this field, so you should be extremely cautious about attributing meaning to any specific piece of behaviour. At a practical level, describing a shape is much easier when you can use your hands.
- *To regulate and control our interactions.* There are many everyday examples of this:
  - when you are at a committee meeting, you try to catch the eye of the chairperson if you want to intervene;
  - if you are speaking to a team member and the discussion is becoming repetitive, you tend to look away and make other movements which suggest that the end of the conversation is due;
  - when talking face-to-face to another person, you show the other person you are about to finish speaking by making sustained eye-contact, as if to say, 'here you are, it's your turn now';
  - if, during supervision, you are trying to persuade a team member to tell you about a difficult problem, you are likely to use lots of head-nods or 'uh-uhs' to maintain the flow of speech.
- *To indicate status and role.* Status is often indicated by the form of dress (for example pin-stripe suit, 'power dressing'), the style of briefcase and the quality of office accommodation. However, there are many more subtle indications. Talking while remaining busy with some other activity is one example, such as when a doctor speaks to an anxious relative while, simultaneously, checking through case notes and avoiding direct eye-contact.

Praise, criticism and reinforcement

One of the pleasures of working life, aside from the salary, is the moment when the boss calls you to one side and congratulates you on a job well done. It costs little or nothing in monetary terms but it can have the most profound impact on the person concerned; it certainly makes the rest of the day go better! The pleasure to be gained through receiving, and giving, praise is something we are introduced to very early in our lives. Few would doubt the power of praise.

Less enjoyable is the experience of being criticised. However, criticism offered in a constructive way is essential if we are to learn from our mistakes. Hard though it usually is, the ability to learn from failure is one of the hallmarks of the successful manager. The benefits of encouraging an open and reflective work culture were described in an earlier chapter; part of this openness is the ability to acknowledge error and to invite and welcome the responses of others. The greatest pain arises in those autocratic organisations where 'fault-finding' is the main managerial pastime.

Our words and actions are usually followed by responses. Some of these responses will encourage us to repeat our behaviour. These are known technically as 'reinforcers', and the process as 'reinforcement'. Most reinforcing responses are rewards which are desirable, such as praise or money.

You should try to make full use of social reinforcement – praise and encouragement, for instance – with your team members in order to maintain morale and good working practices.

Questioning

Questioning can be used for several purposes, most obviously to obtain information. This can be simply factual, such as when you ask for a client's name or age. Alternatively, you may be more interested in discovering how a client feels about his or her situation. In each case, different kinds of question will be most appropriate. It is helpful to distinguish between two types of question:

- *Closed* Closed questions invite a very restricted answer and give very little opportunity for the person to expand on a response. For example:
  'Do you like sugar in coffee?'
  'How old are you?'
  'Where were you born?'
- *Open* These invite a fuller answer which is in the control of the respondent. For example:
  'How do you like to organise your work?'
  'What do you think of the way that child care is organised in this country?'
  'How do you feel you coped this morning?'

Some questions are designed to be impossible to answer without self-incrimination. The model for this is the classic 'Have you stopped beating your wife?' Any response to this kind of closed question will imply guilt. A psychiatrist I knew used to ask patients 'Are you still hearing the voices?' Pity the patient in this situation who had never 'heard voices' – he didn't stand a chance!

Take care to avoid these kinds of trap. It can be easy to ask questions which don't allow the person being questioned a fair chance to explain their point of view. This is a form of oppressive practice.

Listening

Active listening is an under-rated skill. Merely being aware of someone speaking is not the same as listening!

To listen well is to listen actively, i.e. you seek out the message that the other person is trying to get across. You can take this a stage further and try to imagine what it might be like to experience the world through the eyes of the other person – you 'step into their shoes', metaphorically speaking. This process is called *empathy* and is central to all forms of caring whether you are caring for clients or colleagues. To use empathy effectively, you have to be both imaginative and sensitive. Don't assume you know how someone else feels – you never can totally. Always check with the other person whether or not your impressions are accurate.

A competent listener is aware of how the speaker's non-verbal communications relate to what is being said. Are they consistent or does there seem to be a mismatch? For instance, does the person use happy language but look sad?

Because good management depends so much on the ability to listen sensitively, you should spend time trying to improve your skills in this area.

ACTIVITY

For a specified period, say a morning, take note of the way in which others react to you when you are talking to them. Do they really listen or do they just go through the motions? Notice how these different responses make you feel.

ACTIVITY

Make a point of noting how *you* listen to others. Does your listening ability vary with circumstances? For example:

Do you listen more intently when you are talking to the boss, as opposed to a member of your own team?

Is your ability to listen attentively affected when you are

- busy
- tired
- under stress
- bored?

Try discussing your thoughts on this with your team. If relationships in your team are open and reflective, you should be able to do this. More importantly, it then becomes possible for you and your colleagues to be honest with one another. For example, if you are tired, it is better to be able to say to someone, 'Look, I'm really not taking things in at the moment. Do you mind if we speak about this again a little later?'

Opening and closing interactions

How you decide to open a conversation depends very much on the purpose of that conversation. Also important are the existing relationship you have with the person and the context in which the conversation is occurring.

Conversations about routine business matters are likely to open with an exchange of non-verbal communications, such as a hand gesture, eye contact, a smile or a handshake. Verbally, such encounters may begin with the exchange of a few fairly innocuous pleasantries – the weather, sports events, news and so on. There is nothing very remarkable about all this of course; we are all very familiar with these situations. As a manager, however, you need to handle your work relationships in a more deliberate and constructive fashion, to ensure that a conversation gets off to the kind of start which is consistent with what is to follow. If you ignore this maxim, you may create a very uncomfortable situation.

Imagine being asked in to see your manager. He or she seems unusually cordial, asking after your family, holidays and so on. The real reason for the meeting then becomes apparent: to tick you off about an overspend on last month's budget! You feel confused and let down. Avoid treating others in this way by indicating an appropriate tone at the start. If difficult topics are on the agenda, begin in a strictly business-like way and don't encourage your colleague to lower his or her guard. Working within care organisations, with values which emphasise respect for the individual, can sometimes lead to a 'be nice at all costs' approach and a reluctance to deal with problems directly. Always try to ensure that you also adhere to the values of honesty and consistency.

You should pay careful attention to how you choose to close a conversation. Again, you need to create the right tone depending on what you expect to happen next. A straightforward business conversation will be concluded in a manner very different from that used to wind up a discussion about a personal difficulty. Become aware of your own style and try to sense how others react to you. A conversation is like a musical duet. You need to start and finish together: neither stage should come as a surprise! If your time is strictly limited, always let the person know this at the start. By doing so, you will avoid later embarrassment when you need to draw the conversation to a close.

Humour and laughter

Management textbooks rarely include a section on humour. This neglect is surprising because humour and laughter are central to so much of our working and personal lives. Couples marry because they laugh at the same things; workers say that they like the boss because she has a good sense of humour. Few of us would choose to live or work with a 24 hour a day comedian; equally, though, most of us would steer well clear of someone without any humour at all.

Humour has several important functions. We use it to:

- *seek out information* – to find out how well you are accepted in a group by seeing whether others laugh at your jokes;
- *give information* – to convey anxiety, like or dislike, for instance; humour gives some protection allowing you to test out the situation and to make a tactical withdrawal if necessary;
- *provide social control* – for example, to create and maintain a positive working atmosphere or to switch conversation if a difficult topic is coming up;
- *relieve anxiety* – for instance to express relief at the end of a particularly difficult period at work;
- *persuade* – humour can make a message more interesting or memorable (as in this book, I hope!);
- *create a sense of group cohesion* – to strengthen morale and motivation;
- *stay healthy* – laughter has been described as 'internal jogging', helping digestion and exercising internal organs (Hargie 1988); psychologically, humour helps us keep problems in perspective.

ACTIVITY

In the course of a normal working day, notice how frequently humour, smiling and laughter occur. Try to identify how these experiences relate to the functions of humour stated in this chapter.

4.2 Working in teams

Teamwork is vital in all aspects of health and social care. Most people have experienced what it is like to be both a team member and team leader, whether at work or in another situation. According to Charles Handy (1990) there are four important points to remember about teams:

1 Teams are collections of individuals

A team is a group of individuals established to carry out a set of specific functions, whether these are to win a football match or to offer a physiotherapy service in the community. Teams need people who are competent in their jobs. They also need people with different personalities.

Handy suggests that there are four essential roles to be performed in any team:

- *the Captain* – someone who can hold the team together, provide overall leadership and can create an effective working climate;
- *the Administrator* – to keep things tidy, arrange, coordinate, and ensure records are kept efficiently;
- *the Driver* – to provide the energy to see the task through;
- *the Expert* – to offer creative ideas and expertise.

ACTIVITY

Think about the teams which you are part of or know about.

Do the members perform the roles Handy describes?

Do the teams for which you are responsible include these four key roles?

Try to identify where changes should be made in your teams to improve the balance.

You can see from this that it would make no sense to create a team consisting of four 'Experts' – ideas would flow freely for a while but little else would get done. Putting the right team together, then, is very important.

ACTIVITY

Consider the teams you identified for the previous activity.

How far would you say they operated as teams in Handy's terms, or are they really committees under a different name?

Does over-bureaucracy inhibit the workings of any of these teams?

How could you improve teamwork in the teams for which you are responsible?

2 *Teams are not committees*

In Handy's view, committees are 'collections of representatives' put together to reach a solution acceptable to all; they usually have to compromise. By contrast, teams are 'there to win'; they have a sense of common purpose and a team spirit.

Teams should avoid being turned into committees; they should operate with minimum bureaucratic paraphernalia, such as record keeping.

3 *Teams have a life of their own*

Most teams pass through several stages (Tuckman, 1973):

- *Forming* – the warming-up stage; exchange of basic information; initial agreements on how to work.
- *Storming* – the 'shaking-down stage'; differences start to surface and earlier decisions might need changing; this can be traumatic and threaten the team's existence.
- *Norming* – major conflicts have been resolved; ways of working have been agreed; roles have been largely accepted.
- *Performing* – the team now starts to work on its primary purpose.
- *Ending* – some teams will not go through this stage as a whole, but will have to deal with changes of membership at intervals; in other cases, where the team was established to fulfil a specific time-limited function, members will need to come to terms with this stage as a group.

ACTIVITY

When you next join a new team, see if you can identify each of these stages.

If you are setting up a new team yourself, try discussing these stages with members at the start.

If teams are rushed into activity, some of these stages may be missed out which can create problems later. Individuals need time to get to know one another and to allow working relationships to settle down. By being aware of these stages, you can help teams to work through them.

4 *Teams can become too cosy*

After some time, teams can become complacent and less creative. If a team is too intimate, 'groupthink' can develop (Janis, 1971): majority views are accepted without criticism and there is strong peer pressure to conform.

There are several ways in which you can avoid or correct groupthink, for instance:

- ask a team member to be a critical evaluator, i.e. to 'stand back' from the everyday working of the team to try to assess how well it is doing;
- be an impartial leader when decisions are being discussed;
- try splitting the team for a while to work on the same problem;
- encourage the team to regularly review its past performances;
- invite an outsider to attend some of the team meetings.

4.3 Team leadership

Effective leaders do not always take a *leading role*, i.e. they do not always need to be in the limelight or to be dominant people. A good leader in one setting may be relatively ineffective in another.

As a team leader, you need to take into account four related areas of leadership:

- *What needs to be done (the task)* Does the task suggest an appropriate leadership style? For example, do you have to work to a very short deadline, or is the task longer term?
- *How the team should be established and maintained (the team)* Have you put the best team together? How can you ensure that the team passes successfully through the stages described by Tuckman earlier in this section? Do you establish clear rules of working for the team?
- *The development of the individual team members (the individuals)* What are the individual needs of team members? Do you pay attention to the performance of individuals and intervene to provide support when necessary?
- *The context within which leadership has to take place (the context)* What is the dominant leadership style in your organisation? How much variation would be tolerated? Have you been given sufficient resources to do the job?

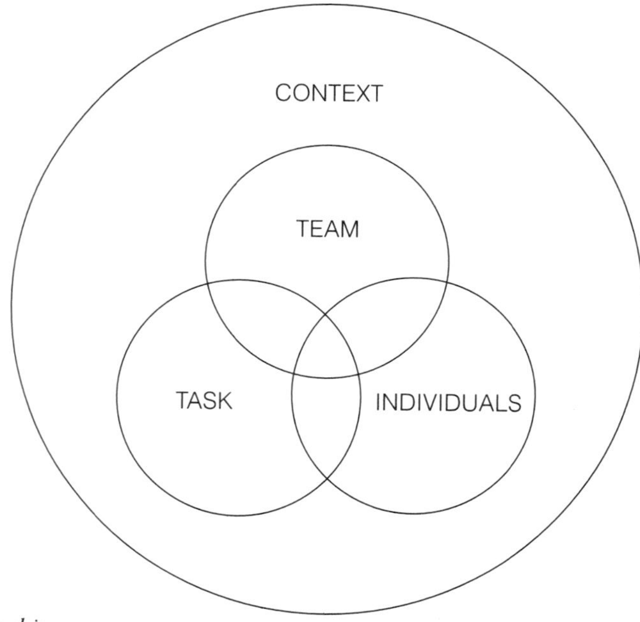

Team leadership

Effective leadership

No-one will ever produce the definitive list of effective leadership behaviours. However, the following list includes some of the most important.

Effective team leaders:

- demonstrate a commitment to the basic values of the team and the organisation (for example valuing the individual, innovation, meeting community needs);

- oversee the work of the team and ensure that targets are met;
- are flexible in style (for example by knowing when to intervene personally and when to let the team get on with the task);
- establish clear objectives;
- provide helpful conditions for effective teamwork (for example by obtaining adequate material resources and by arguing the team's case in the organisation as a whole);
- demonstrate how they value each individual team member;
- recognise and use the potential and excellence in each person;
- are open to new ideas.

ACTIVITY

Look back at the eight characteristics of effective team leadership outlined in this section. How effective are your own team leadership skills?

Try rating your performance on each of these characteristics. For each characteristic, decide whether you are 'satisfied or dissatisfied' with your current performance. If dissatisfied, how do you plan to improve?

- demonstrate a commitment to the team's values;
- meet targets;
- flexible in style;
- establish clear objectives;
- provide helpful conditions;
- value each team member;
- recognise the potential in staff;
- open to new ideas.

ACTIVITY

Select two or three major areas of work, or major decisions, where you have found it hard to get agreement with your team.

- How did you react to these difficulties?
- Could you have handled them better in the light of experience?
- If so, what would you have done differently on each occasion?

4.4 Enhancing relationships with your own manager

For any organisation to be effective, managers at all levels should try to develop constructive working relationships. There will be times when you disagree with decisions made by your own manager. There will be others when, however hard you try, you cannot seem to extract any decision at all! By contrast, you will experience periods when everything goes like clockwork.

There are several ways to develop and enhance the relationship with your immediate manager. You should try to:

- *provide appropriate information at the correct level of detail and time* – don't pass on every detail, it isn't necessary. Discuss the issues if you are unsure. You need to develop a 'sixth sense' about when an apparently minor problem could become a major one;
- *accept the situation when your ideas are not supported* – this does not mean that you should not pursue your argument vigorously: you should. But it does mean that you should recognise when the argument is over – continued resistance will lead to a very sore head! You might then be able to provide alternative proposals which will succeed.
- *keep disagreements at the professional level* – avoid making problems personal. It should be possible to disagree without falling out. Major problems in this area should be discussed directly with your manager.
- *be open and honest* – avoid pretending things are going well when they are not; admit ignorance when you have to.
- *keep your sense of humour!*

ACTIVITY

How effective is your relationship with your immediate manager?

Are there areas you would like to improve? What are they? How could you go about improving things?

4.5 Respecting and valuing differences

One of your tasks is to ensure that individual differences are valued and respected within your team. History tells us that differences between people have often led to serious inequalities and discrimination. Groups of people who are noticeably different tend to suffer in particular – for example on grounds of sex, age, race, colour and disability.

By recognising the dangers and remaining vigilant, you can help to minimise discrimination. This is not just a case of watching for discrimination in others but of recognising and combating it in yourself.

The health and social care sectors need a diverse workforce for many reasons, for example:

- care is provided for all social groups and the workforce should reflect this range;
- the care sector should lead by example – it should aim to be a model for the rest of society in how to combat discrimination;
- the sector needs to be able to draw on the widest range of different skills, backgrounds and approaches to deal with its problems and challenges – for example women are under-represented as managers in many areas.

ACTIVITY

Think about your own workforce. How diverse would you say it is? Which groups are particularly under-represented, and at what levels in the organisation?

You should incorporate an equal opportunities philosophy into your everyday way of managing – by aiming to be fair and objective to all members of your team – and by challenging discrimination whenever it occurs. You are required to operate within the law and it is illegal to discriminate on grounds of race, sex or marital status. Remember that it is the *effect* of your actions which is considered, not their intention – inadvertent discrimination is still illegal.

Many groups in society are not protected explicitly by the law, for example older people, gays, lesbians, and people with HIV/AIDS. However, many employers are trying to extend their policies beyond the bare legal requirements and establish themselves as equal opportunity employers.

Remember that equal opportunity is the right of everyone, beyond those groups identified specifically. Accent, educational background, appearance, social class, wealth, interests – all of these qualities and characteristics can be used to oppress and discriminate against others.

There are many practical ways in which you can promote equal opportunities in your job:

1 *Be self-aware*

Examine your own attitudes frequently, especially when you have to make important decisions about, for example, recruitment, promotion or setting up a new work group. Ask yourself how you made your decisions. Were they entirely objective? It can help to discuss these issues with your own manager or with a colleague.

2 *Be a good role model*

Question colleagues about their attitudes and decisions. Make sure that equal opportunity issues are on the agenda at meetings, or are considered during discussions. If you have to write, say, an annual report on your area of responsibility, include a section on equal opportunities.

3 *Support your 'at-risk' staff*

Some members of your staff may feel that they are at-risk of, or are actually experiencing, discrimination or prejudice – whether at work or outside. Your support will be invaluable and you can show it by your general attitude and decisions, and by being a willing listener to those who want to talk about how they feel. Create a working ethos that encourages the open expression of feelings of this kind. Suppressing this issue does not make it go away – it merely leads to a bigger problem later.

Identifying groups of people who are at particular risk of discrimination has allowed progress to be made on equal opportunities. However, there are considerable dangers when these labels are applied to individuals. Do not assume, for example, that all black people feel discriminated against; or indeed that all black people categorise themselves as 'black'. Similarly, not all 'disabled' people see themselves as 'disabled'; people over the age of 65 do not all think of themselves as 'old'. In supporting your staff, you must try to see around these labels to the person beyond.

4 *Challenge discrimination and prejudice in others*

Acts of discrimination are unacceptable in the workplace. As a manager, you must never ignore such acts. Discriminatory behaviour might include open abuse or harassment; sometimes it can take the form of 'throw-away' remarks. These apparently harmless comments can be the most difficult to deal with because they are often ambiguous and it is quite likely that the person confronted will dispute your interpretation of events. Even if you are proved wrong in your interpretation, you will have been right to have raised the issue and to have drawn your concerns to the attention of the person involved.

5 Challenge the organisation's policies

The policies and procedures of the organisation should also be kept under scrutiny. This kind of awareness has led to many official documents now being produced in a variety of languages to suit the needs of the local community, for example the Charters developed by health authorities and other agencies.

If you detect an unmet need of this kind, you should raise it with the appropriate person in your organisation. In many situations, communicating a service to a wider range of people makes good business, as well as good moral, sense.

Every organisation should develop an equal opportunities policy and all staff should know and own it. In addition to a broad policy statement, there should be additional guidance – a *Code of Practice* perhaps – setting out what the policy means in practice. Procedures for monitoring the effectiveness of the policy and the codes are needed as well.

ACTIVITY

You are a Occupational Therapist working in a unit for the physically handicapped. Marjorie is an occupational therapy helper in your team. She was born in the UK of black Nigerian parents and is the only person from an 'ethnic minority' working in the unit. She has come to see you very upset, complaining that certain colleagues have been making racist remarks in her presence. She was passing through the staff room when she heard snatches of conversation including the words 'golliwog' and 'thick'.

When you challenge the three staff concerned about this, they say that they were sharing childhood experiences – several of them happened to have owned golliwog dolls. No-one can remember using the word 'thick'. They don't appear to take the complaint at all seriously; one in particular starts to talk about Marjorie as being over-sensitive and as 'having a chip'.

Consider the following questions.

- What would your aims be in trying to resolve this problem?
- What further actions do you need to take? What are your priorities?
- How should you go about supporting Marjorie?
- What are your responsibilities towards the other staff – both the three you have seen and the others in the unit?
- What do you tell your own manager?

ACTIVITY

Obtain a copy of your own organisation's equal opportunities policy. Answer the following questions:

- Do you feel a sense of ownership for this document?
- Does the policy cover more than the legal minimum? If so, which other groups are protected from discrimination by this policy?
- Is there a code of practice or similar guidance available?
- Who would you approach if you wanted to ask about the interpretation of the policy?
- How do you ensure that your staff are made aware of the policy?
- How often do you refer to the policy in everyday work?
- Have you or your staff received training in equal opportunities?
- How would you improve the present policy and guidance?

ACTIVITY

Discrimination can be very subtle. Consider the following possibilities. Do they apply to you or your colleagues? Try to discuss your thoughts with a colleague or your supervisor.

- When involved in discussions, do you have a tendency to look more at the men or the women in the group?
- Do you sometimes treat people from other cultures in stereotypical ways, for example by using such expressions as 'Italians are very emotional, aren't they?' or 'We could do with more Chinese nurses here – they're so hard working!' or by assuming that all Asian clients want to eat curry, for instance.
- Do you sometimes use technical words when you know that some members of the team will not understand what you mean? Why might you do this?

ACTIVITY

As a playgroup leader, you have taken on a new helper, Paul, a young man in his twenties. This is the first time that you have employed a man in this capacity. After a week or two, several female members of your team tell you that some mothers have remarked that they are 'a bit worried' about having a man working with their children.

Consider these questions:

- Do you think that this is a problem or will it 'go away' if left alone?
- What are your responsibilities towards:
  - Paul
  - the mothers
  - the children
  - the other staff?
- What actions will you now take and why?

IMPRESSIONS FROM AN OFFICE

The family picture is on HIS desk. A solid, responsible family man.	The family picture is on HER desk. Family will come before her career.
HIS desk is cluttered. A hard worker and a busy man.	HER desk is cluttered. A disorganised scatterbrain.
HE is talking with his co-workers. He must be discussing the latest deal.	SHE is talking to her co-workers. She must be gossiping.
HE's not at his desk. He must be at a meeting.	SHE's not at her desk. She must be in the ladies' room.
HE's not in the office. He's meeting customers.	SHE's not in the office. She must be out shopping.
HE's having lunch with the boss. He's on the way up.	SHE's having lunch with the boss. They must be having an affair.
The boss criticised HIM. He'll improve his performance.	The boss criticised HER. She'll be very upset.
HE got an unfair deal. Did he get angry?	SHE got an unfair deal. Did she cry?
HE's getting married. He'll get more settled.	SHE's getting married. She'll get pregnant and leave.
HE's going on a business trip. It's good for his career.	SHE's going on a business trip. What will her husband say?

(From 'Management Men and Women: Closed versus Open Doors', by Natasha Josefowitz, *Harvard Business Review*, 58, 4, Sept/Oct 1980, pp. 57–62. Quoted in an article by Roz Langtry (1990) 'A man's world?', *Insight*, 5, 21, pp. 24–25).

4.6 Handling conflicts

Conflict at work is commonplace, as it is in life generally. It can be positive and constructive, or it can be very destructive.

Levels of conflict

You will meet conflict at different levels:

Intrapersonal

This is where the conflict exists *within* the individual. You may have experienced it as 'divided loyalties'.

Example
You discover that one of your team, whom you have worked with and trusted for many years, has been submitting false travel claims. You have signed these for the past six months without adequate checking. You are torn between your loyalty to your colleague and your loyalty to your employer.

Interpersonal

This occurs when conflict occurs *between* two or more people.

> *Example*
> Two senior care assistants are responsible for the day-to-day organisation of an activity programme for clients in a residential care home. They work on opposite shifts and have quite different views about what approach to take, leaving the clients confused about what to expect.

Intergroup

Conflict between groups can arise where different groups are fighting over the same territory.

> *Example*
> In a community service for people with mental health problems, there is a long-running battle between occupational therapists and physiotherapists as to who should organise and run relaxation groups.

Sources of conflict

Conflict has different sources:

Personality

Some people seem to have a high level of 'natural' aggression – a need to dominate others.

> *Example*
> Alan is an ambitious staff nurse but is unpopular with his peers. His seems interested only in how quickly he can impress his boss and 'get on'. When he is on duty, his colleagues are tense and uncomfortable, always expecting a row to occur.

Competition for scarce resources

Care sector organisations have to cope with many key resources being in short supply – money, trained staff, time, for instance.

> *Example*
> Due to cutbacks, departmental heads in a social services department are constantly looking for ways to acquire extra resources at the expense of colleagues. Some of the tactics are ethically questionable, for example spreading rumours about other departments' problems.

Poorly defined responsibilities

Conflict will occur if the boundaries of a job are unclear.

> *Example*
> Following reorganisation of a large day centre for older people, a former line manager is given responsibility for 'projects'. Armed with only a vague job description, she runs into problems with colleagues who consider she hasn't got a real job. Increasingly, she feels the same.

Clashes of values

We can never completely share our values and philosophies with others. However, sometimes these lead to serious difficulties in the workplace.

> *Example*
> Staff in a playgroup often encourage girls to dress up in boys' clothes, and vice versa. They see this as both fun and as a way of addressing male/female issues at an early age. However, some parents have objected to this very strongly, threatening to withdraw their children if it does not stop at once.

Positive outcomes

Conflict can lead to *positive* outcomes:

- *increased creativity* – conflict can force new solutions to old problems;
- *expression of emotion* – conflict can build up tension which needs to be released before progress can be made;
- *greater awareness of self and others* – a clearer, more realistic view of relationships and events can result;
- *more effective ways of dealing with conflict* – conflict management may become part of the way the organisation works.

Dealing with conflict

There are several strategies for you to choose from:

- *Identifying a shared goal* – conflicting parties can be drawn together by discovering or creating a shared goal that they can both work towards. In this way, trust can grow and develop.
- *Confrontation* – this involves airing the problem with the conflicting parties, face-to-face. For this to work, you have to create a positive atmosphere, based on mutual respect and a desire to solve the problem.
- *Compromise* – in this solution, each person gives up something and gains something. This may be the only answer in some situations, for example when two staff are demanding more resources for their activities than the budget will allow; if both activities must take place, then compromise is the only way through.
- *Third party intervention* – some conflicts cannot be resolved directly by the people concerned. In these cases, you may need to introduce a third party, your own manager perhaps, to help solve the problem or to make the final decision.

Approaches to avoid

Try to avoid these approaches:

- *Denying* – this is the failure to accept that conflict exists at all.
- *Putting-off* – avoiding attempts to resolve the conflict positively; making excuses, such as 'no time' or 'it will go away, given time'.
- *Taking the easy way out* – taking the line of least resistance, regardless of the longer term consequences.
- *Imposing a solution* – imposing a solution to the conflict from above: the underlying problems remain hidden only to surface later.

4.7 Grievances and disciplinary action

ACTIVITY

You must be familiar with your organisation's disciplinary and grievance procedures. No one can remember every detail and you must ensure that you refer to them whenever a potential grievance or disciplinary matter is anticipated.

Do you know how to access all the relevant policies and procedures?

Do you know from whom to seek advice if you have a problem with interpreting these documents?

So far, this chapter has looked at some of the issues you need to consider when managing relationships in teams, some of the problems that can occur and how you might handle them. However, from time to time, the approaches described will be unsuccessful. This section deals with grievance procedures and disciplinary action. When either action becomes necessary, it indicates that the behaviour of employee or employer has been seen as unacceptable; it might also suggest that the usual informal systems for handling conflict and exerting control have broken down.

Employers need to devise policies and procedures which conform to current legislation and codes of practice, and are agreed by the relevant trades unions. You need to be familiar with the policies used by your own organisation. Failure to implement procedures carefully, fairly and promptly has been the reason for many failures at local appeals hearings or at Industrial Tribunals.

Grievance

Grievances are brought by employees against their employers. They are a way of complaining about some aspect of employment, for example sexual harassment, changes in working conditions or salary gradings.

Formal grievance procedures should set out what employees should do in a series of stages. Most procedures recognise that, in the normal course of work, employees will wish to question decisions made by their employers. They should first speak to their immediate manager. You should reassure your team that you expect them to bring their concerns or complaints to you in the first instance. There are exceptions to this, such as if a member of staff accuses you of racial harassment. Under these circumstances, it would be reasonable for the person to take the matter up with your boss.

If the problem cannot be resolved at immediate manager level, it must be referred to higher management in accordance with the organisation's procedures.

Disciplinary procedures

Staff do not always perform to an acceptable standard. These lapses can be relatively minor, for example answering the phone rather abruptly, or they can be very serious, such as abusing clients or claiming false expenses. Minor problems will be identified as a result of day-to-day monitoring and should be dealt with when they occur. They may also be raised during professional supervision and staff appraisal.

When misconduct is too serious to be dealt with informally, you will need to invoke formal procedures. You should remember that every time you start a disciplinary procedure, it could result in the eventual dismissal of the employee. Fairness and the ability to be reasonable are paramount at every stage.

Most disciplinary procedures have several stages. At each stage, the employee has the right to be accompanied and advised by a trade union representative or a friend. Many procedures also give the employee the right of appeal at each stage; this helps an employer demonstrate the fairness of the process. The complexity of the procedures will depend on the size of the organisation – the larger the organisation, the more detailed the procedures need to be.

Typical stages are as follows:

1 *Informal verbal warnings* – given by the immediate manager with no formal record being kept.
2 *Formal verbal warnings* – these follow a formal disciplinary interview and are recorded on the employee's personal file for a specified period; the employee will be told clearly what he or she has to do to demonstrate acceptable behaviour. Support and guidance should also be offered to help the person meet these goals.
3 *Written warnings* – if the poor performance persists, a written warning may be given. Again, employees should be told what they have to do to avoid further action. Some organisations allow for two written warnings – a first and a final; others have only one. A written warning will last for a specified period (for example, twelve months), after which it can be removed (expunged) from the personal file.
4 *Dismissal* – if employees have failed to improve after the implementation of the organisation's disciplinary procedure, they can be fairly dismissed.

The starting point for disciplinary action depends on the seriousness of the misconduct. Extreme cases, such as the physical abuse of clients, will result in summary dismissal on the grounds of gross misconduct. This kind of behaviour causes a fundamental break in the relationship between employee and employer; as a result, the contract of employment has been destroyed.

Always discuss a disciplinary situation with your own manager – it can be difficult to decide on the appropriate level of discipline to take and mistakes can be costly to the organisation.

One of the more difficult problems you may have to face is when a team member develops a bad sickness/absence record. Sometimes, simply drawing attention to a poor record will result in an improvement. In other cases, an extensive sickness/absence record may lead to dismissal on grounds of incapability to carry out the job. You need to ensure that you have very accurate records available before beginning a procedure which could lead to dismissal.

In some cases, an employee may be suspended on full pay while an investigation takes place, for example, when one member of staff accuses another of ill-treating a client. It may take some time to interview witnesses, if any, and it is often fairest to all concerned to suspend the accused person, usually on full pay. This allows emotions to subside and a more objective investigation to be carried out.

Sometimes, disciplinary problems are due to factors outside work: sickness, domestic stresses and so on. In such cases, it is important to advise counselling or other help at appropriate stages. Remember that the overall aim of disciplinary action is to help staff improve their performance, not to sack them.

ACTIVITY

Mary is a health care assistant in a maternity unit. She has a poor lateness record. You have had several words with her about this and have given her two informal verbal warnings. She explains that she has two very young children and that it is very difficult for her to arrive by exactly 07.30, although she always assures you she will do better in future.

You have decided that the next stage must be a disciplinary interview. You have informed Mary of this and invited her to bring along a trade union representative or friend. You have asked the personnel officer to be present too.

Think through how you want this interview to proceed, using the following questions as a guide.

- Where would you conduct this interview?
- How would you start the interview?
- What attitude should you adopt?
- What are you trying to achieve by this interview?
- How would you conclude the interview?
- What would you put in a letter confirming the decisions made at interview?

A stock form of disciplinary action?

Reading on ...

★ A range of personnel and other employment guides are available from Croner Publications (tel: 0181 547 3333).

★ Handy, Charles (1993) *Understanding Organisations*, Penguin Books Ltd, Harmondsworth.

★ Handy, Charles (1990) *Inside Organisations: 21 ideas for managers*, BBC Books, London. This contains the thoughts of an experienced manager and is entertaining as well as thoughtful.

★ Hargie, Owen (ed.) (1988) *A Handbook of Communication Skills*, Routledge, London

★ Janis, Irving (1971) 'Groupthink', *Psychology Today*, Volume 5, November 1971, pp. 43–46, 74–76.

★ Tuckman B. (1973) in Napier, Rodney W. and Gerfhenfeld, Matti K. (eds) *Group Theory and Experience*, Houghton Mifflin, Boston.

5 Managing communication

Organisations survive and prosper through their ability to communicate a wide range of information. However, communication is a complex activity and subject to regular breakdowns, as most of us are only too aware.

Effective communication is limited by the amount of information we can deal with at one time. Too much information moving around an organisation puts managers under great pressure. It gets harder to decide which information is important to you and which you can or should ignore. You need to find ways of dealing with these increasing demands without becoming overwhelmed.

In every aspect of your work – decision-making, marketing, recording care, training – you depend on the communication of accurate information. As the care sector grows more complex, organisations need increasing amounts of relevant and precise information to manage their affairs. This information is not only increasing in volume but is also moving faster (faxes, computers, electronic mail and so on).

In addition to these general trends, information in the care sector often has special characteristics, for example:

- much information is confidential, for example details about clients, discussions between professionals;
- information can be emotive – it can deal with illness, birth and death; complaints from clients or relatives;
- information often has to be managed accurately under stressful conditions – for example reading and responding to drug prescriptions in an understaffed ward.
- information comes from a huge variety of sources – from clients, professionals, relatives, professional journals, government circulars and EU directives.

Increasingly, you also need to know about developments in information technology. The latest technologies can be very seductive, however. Most of us have met the enthusiast who abuses information technology by over-communicating or using it inappropriately – for instance word-processing a memorandum when a simple phone call would do, or producing complex statistics which few understand and even fewer find relevant. Misusing technology is expensive and can cause other staff unnecessary work. Keep in mind the following principles. They apply to the use of all types of information.

Information should be:

- *relevant* – keep to the point;
- *clear and unambiguous* – vocabulary, sentence structure, diagrams, charts, etc. should be as straightforward as possible;

ACTIVITY

Examine the amount of information you receive regularly in the course of a working day.

- Do you think that all of the communications you receive, such as memos, reports, telephone calls, are strictly necessary?
- How do you cope when the volume increases? For example, how do you prioritise?
- Discuss this problem with some of your colleagues. You may find they have different ways of coping which you might want to try.

- *accurate* – check facts before you use them;
- *on target* – don't communicate too widely; decide who really needs to know, the others have got enough on their plates already!
- *sufficient* – cover what is necessary, no more no less;
- *in an appropriate format* – more significant since the use of computers has become more widespread; for example check on compatibility of hardware and software;
- *retrievable* – is information easily accessible to those who need it?
- *economic* – communication costs money; don't waste, for example the paper used for internal memos can be cheaper than that used for letters to external agencies;
- *empathic* – an unusual word to use in this context but it is essential; put yourself in the position of the person who will receive your information and adapt what you communicate accordingly; more empathy means less wasted time and money.

5.1 Presenting information

Managers have to present information in both written or oral form. This section describes how to write a report and how to make an oral presentation – two of the most demanding forms of communication. By mastering both, you will be learning many vital skills of communication in general.

Writing reports

Report-writing is an essential skill. Remember that all forms of written communication can be read and re-read. Any mistakes will be there for others to see for as long as the recipient chooses. Your credibility is at stake so take pride in improving and developing your writing skills. The possible reasons for writing a report include:

- making a case for resources;
- dealing with a complaint;
- arguing for a new care practice;
- evaluating a service;
- acting on a request from senior management.

Whatever the purpose of your reports, they should be:

- clear;
- concise;
- logical;
- relevant;
- supported by evidence and rational argument;
- courteous;
- well presented.

Reports should conform to the standard rules of grammar, spelling and punctuation. If you have a problem with written work, get appropriate help before finishing your report. Most word processors have spell checks built in and some have grammar checks, too; if not, use a dictionary and a basic language textbook. A friend with a good command of the language is a valuable asset. Details of several helpful books are included at the end of this chapter.

Use the following report structure as a guide. It suggests a structure for a lengthy formal report. You will almost certainly want to change it to suit your own particular needs.

1 *Front cover ('title fly')* – titles should be factual and indicate what is covered at a glance. For example:
   'Caring for older people at Daneleigh Park in the year 2000 – a proposal to diversify into home care.'
   Avoid brief 'tabloid'-type titles, such as:
   'New meals in the millennium!'
2 *Title page* – title plus details of author and who the report is for:
   'Caring for older people at Daneleigh Park in the year 2000 – a proposal to diversify into home care.'
   Prepared for J M Palmer, Managing Director, Royal Oak Care.
   Prepared by J M McCleod, Assistant Manager, Daneleigh Park.
3 *Table of Contents* – this should include page numbers. If the report includes tables, charts, diagrams and illustrations, you should prepare a separate list of contents for these.
4 *Summary (also called a synopsis or abstract)* – this summarises all the major information, conclusions and recommendations. Remember that this may be the only part to be read by a busy senior manager. Ensure it includes the key points. Some reports summarise the recommendations in full at this stage so that readers can grasp the implications at the outset; the arguments for the recommendations will be contained in the main body of the report.
5 *Main body of the report* – the arrangement of the main body depends on the type of report and personal preference, unless you have to work to specific guidelines prepared by your employer. Generally, reports should follow a logical structure to help the reader through the maze of the argument. This is very much in the interests of the report writer, especially where the intended outcome is more resources! The main body might contain:
   (a) *Introduction* – origin and purpose of the report, its aims and terms of reference; sources of information and how it was collected; structure of the report.
   (b) *Main section* – presents information collected; links it with the problem; analyses the problem and offers options. Data may be presented in a variety of forms – tables, charts, diagrams, etc. Ensure that data presentation is very clear and relevant to the problem in hand. Computer programmes make it very easy to analyse complex data in a vast number of ways. However, don't include irrelevant data analysis. If your main section is lengthy, you might want to summarise each section; any device which helps the reader to follow your thinking will help your cause.
6 *Conclusions* – this section contains your conclusions based on the evidence presented in the main body of the report.
7 *Recommendations* – these are your suggested actions based on the conclusions. You may wish to prioritise your recommendations to highlight particular actions.
8 *Appendix* – this is used for supplementary information. Examples include minutes of meetings, questionnaires or other reports.
9 *Bibliography* – this is a list of sources, some of which will have been referred to in the report. List all the significant journals, books and other sources you have used to prepare the report. There are conventions for presenting references and bibliographies. Look at the ways in which professional journals use references and bibliographies, adopt a style you

feel comfortable with. The method used in this book would be acceptable in most cases.

10 *Index* – necessary for long reports using many technical terms. Make sure the topics are listed in strict alphabetical order.

Don't expect to produce an acceptable report at one sitting. Plan to produce an initial draft followed by one, possibly two more before the final version emerges. Word processors help you to speed up the task considerably.

Oral presentations

You use an oral presentation to get across your ideas to others using the spoken word, supported as necessary by visual aids. You should prepare very carefully because stumbling over your words and losing the point will make you less effective and damage your credibility.

Planning

Sometimes a report will have to be delivered in the course of a meeting and you will have a very limited time to get your message across. On other occasions, you will have longer but you should still be concise. Like the written report, the structure of your presentation must be logical. However, whereas a written report usually convinces through the power of its argument, the success of a presentation often depends on how interesting it is and how well you keep the attention of the audience.

Notes

Always prepare notes to keep you on track and to make sure you cover all the important issues. You need not follow these slavishly but don't trust your memory to get you through.

Oral presentations need good organisation

There are different ways of preparing notes. Probably the most usual is to write the key points on small cards, commonly 5" × 3". These can be held quite discreetly and changed quickly and easily. If you prefer to use A4 sheets, you will need somewhere to rest them – avoid holding them while you talk.

However you record your notes, be sure to use capital letters or coloured highlights for the main points – these will help you find your way back if you get lost or distracted. If your audience is likely to question you about the detail of what you are saying, you should have extra documents nearby but keep them separate from your notes.

Resources

Decide on the physical resources you will need, for example:

- What seating arrangements do you want? Is the size of the room adequate?
- Will you want audio-visual aids, for example overhead projector, slide projector? (These are referred to again later in this chapter.)
- Do you want any handouts or other photocopies prepared in advance?
- Is there a clock in the room or do you need to use your own watch? Always put it where you can see it easily.

Personal presentation

Improve your presentation skills by taking note of the following points:

- *confidence* – you need to appear reasonably confident; good preparation is the best insurance policy;
- *appearance* – choose your dress to fit the expectations of the audience and the occasion;
- *general body language* – weigh up whether it is better to sit or stand; standing can give the best results, even with a relatively small group;
- *movement* – keep wandering under control! Some movement helps to maintain concentration; too much and listeners soon become distracted and irritated;
- *facial expression* – use eye-contact and an interested expression to show your involvement;
- *voice* – listen to yourself on tape before exposing yourself to the wider world; try to include adequate variation in tone, speed and emphasis;
- *avoid irritating habits* – fiddling with a pencil or papers; using too many 'ers'; making annoying hand movements. Ask a good friend for an honest opinion; eventually you will become aware of them yourself.

ACTIVITY

Listen to your favourite broadcasters on TV or radio.

- What is it about their presentations that makes you listen?
- How would you compare your own performance?
- How would you like to change to improve your own delivery?

Be prepared to try out different approaches and borrow the techniques of others.

Structure

The opening of an oral presentation is crucial: as much for your benefit as for that of the audience. A well prepared opening helps to settle you down. It could be a quiet start, gradually building to a crescendo, or it might begin with a bang, go quiet, and then finish with a flourish!

Remind the audience of where you are in the presentation. Remember that when you are listening you don't have the benefit of the written word – you can't check or re-read at the time – so 'signpost' the presentation as you go along. You may find this tedious but your audience will appreciate it.

End on time. Keep your watch, or a clock, in sight and don't drift on, even when you think the audience wants you to – you can guarantee that the majority would prefer to go to lunch! Prepare an effective ending. Summarise what you have said and conclude with energy – perhaps with a humorous comment or reference back to your opening material.

Visual aids

Use visual aids when you can. They hold the audience's attention and you can use them to summarise material very effectively. There are several types, including:

- *Whiteboard* – the simplest, most flexible method; the modern version of the blackboard, the whiteboard is cleaner, clearer and more attractive. If possible, you should give yourself time to practise because writing vertically in letters large enough to see from some distance is a difficult skill.
- *Flipchart* – the paper equivalent of the whiteboard but smaller. You can't rub this out so be sure you feel confident about your writing.
- *Overhead projector (OHP)* – although this is more complicated technically, it has the advantage that you can prepare all your visual aids before the presentation. OHPs use special transparencies, square or rectangular sheets of acetate (usually called *acetates*) – that you use to write or draw on with special pens (*OHP* or *acetate* pens); these are then projected (and enlarged) on to a screen. The overall results can be impressive and worth the effort. But again, practise first.
- *Slides* – use these where you need high quality reproductions of specific and realistic illustrations. For text, the OHP is better.
- *Video* – this can often induce sleep rather than stimulation. You must be sure you know why you are using video. Used well, it can involve the audience and provoke strong reactions. Always introduce a video and explain what the audience is expected to do, for example express an opinion, draw a conclusion.

5.2 Managing meetings

ACTIVITY

List all the meetings you attend on a regular basis. Make a note of the official title of each meeting. Business meetings are intended to have a purpose.

- What would you say is the main purpose of each meeting?
- Is a meeting the only way to achieve this purpose?
- What alternative methods could be used to achieve the same purpose, for example telephone conversations, small group discussions, exchange of memos?

Meetings are like taxes: we've got to have them but we wish there were fewer! Every organisation depends upon meetings of its staff to fulfil many of its basic functions. As part of the management structure, you will be expected both to attend and to run meetings – you need to be able to get the most out of them.

All meetings should have a business purpose but they also fulfil social needs. This secondary function should not be dismissed out of hand because social interaction is a necessary part of everyday working life. However, try to keep the business purpose to the fore.

You may call a meeting to discuss a particular issue or because you have been delegated this task by senior management. Factors to consider are:

- *Why?* Be clear about why the meeting has been called.
- *Who?* Invite people who are essential and who can contribute effectively; keep the number down to the minimum needed to ensure adequate representation and credibility.
- *When?* Give adequate notice. Demands on everyone's time are increasing so give as much advance notice as possible. Key people should be sounded out early enough so that they can check their diaries. When you have settled on a date, confirm this in writing as soon as possible; this may be by sending out the agenda for the meeting.
- *Where?* Book an appropriate room for the meeting.

Chairing meetings

Chairing a meeting for the first time is often a daunting experience. As chairperson, you are carrying out a formal role and this can feel awkward at first, especially when colleagues are present. However, it pays to adopt the formal conventions: you will be able to get through the substance of the meeting in a more business-like way. Effective meetings need thorough preparation. Firstly, this means drawing up an appropriate agenda.

Prepare an effective agenda

Every meeting should have an agenda. Even informal meetings must have some direction. In the case of formal meetings, an informative agenda:

- gives the date, time and precise location of the meeting (maps should be sent to outside visitors if necessary);
- allows people to prepare for the meeting;
- indicates the priority and purpose of each topic;
- suggests timings.

ACTIVITY

Look at the following agendas. What are the strengths and weaknesses of each?

Staff Meeting
7 February 09.30
Seminar Room

Agenda

1. Minutes of the last meeting
2. Budget
3. Staffing issues
4. Training

Staff meeting
7 February 09.30–11.30
Seminar Room

Agenda

5mins	*1.0*	*Apologies for absence*
10mins	*2.0*	*Minutes of the last meeting (held on 9 March)*
15mins	*3.0*	*Matters arising (not already on the agenda)*
25mins	*4.0*	*Budget*
		4.1 To consider current budget and plan for year's end
		4.2 To receive and discuss draft budget for the next year
20mins	*5.0*	*Staffing issues*
		5.1 New appointments made:
		Mark Palmer
		Helen Toro
		5.2 Bids for an increase in establishment
30mins	*6.0*	*Training*
		6.1 To discuss training needs of clerical staff
		6.2 To agree staff development plan for professional staff (previously distributed)
10mins	*7.0*	*Any other business*
	8.0	*Date of next meeting*

Running the meeting

A good chairperson manages the meeting with a mixture of firmness, tolerance and good humour. The aim is to get the most out of the people present in order to achieve the aims of the meeting. There are several techniques you can use:

- *Ensure that a formal record is made of the meeting (the 'minutes')* – formal committees usually have a designated minute-taker; in less formal meetings you may need to arrange for one of the participants to take the minutes.
- *Follow the agenda* – don't drift off the topic; you will only waste time and risk not achieving the meeting's aims.
- *Establish the purpose of the meeting at the start* – this helps to remind participants why they are there which busy people will find useful.
- *Keep to time* – nothing irritates participants more than a chairperson who (a) starts the meeting late or (b) lets meetings over-run.
- *Introduce each topic as you reach it* – you may need to present background facts or the broad context; you could use an OHP for this or give out handouts.
- *Limit discussion* – some topics need full discussion but you should not let the debate continue beyond the point where all major issues have been raised.
- *Take notes* – you should take brief notes yourself (in addition to the formal minutes); these will help you summarise the discussion at the end of each agenda item.
- *Clarify communications* – confusion and muddle can arise in meetings; it is your job as chairperson to point these out and try to straighten them out.
- *Confirm the minutes as soon as possible after the meeting* – the minute-taker should give you a first draft of the minutes within a day or two of the meeting; if it is left longer you may not be able to recall the discussion accurately. You should agree the final draft as soon as possible so that the final version can be sent to the participants in the meeting.
- *Use a standard format for minutes* – some organisations have their own format to which all meetings must conform.
- *Keep minutes as short as possible* – if you don't, they won't be read. Ensure that the minutes record:
  - past actions taken
  - key issues raised
  - future actions agreed
  - who will take action and when (best put in a separate column on the right hand side of the paper, or underlined).

5.3 Managing information systems

> 'There are few greater liberating forces than the sharing of information. There is no such thing as "delegation" or "motivation" without extensive information.'
>
> Peters 1988

Many of the changes that have taken place in health and social care have happened as a result of the revolution in information systems and information technology. Market developments in the National Health Service, quality assurance systems, accurate budget monitoring – none of these would be possible without ample and accurate information. The purchaser–provider split discussed in Chapter 3 relies upon both sides gathering relevant information. Government now publishes a wide range of performance indicators for public consumption based on data collected from the care sector, for instance league tables of waiting list times, ratios of the numbers of doctors to members of the public, relative costs of operations.

Smaller organisations have also benefited from developments in information systems, for example patient/client records, staff records, budget control and report writing. Many care and nursing homes, day centres and nurseries have their own personal computers (PCs) that they can use for word-processing, setting up databases or spreadsheets. These are explained later in this chapter.

The main reason for this information explosion is the widespread use of computers. By using computers, information can be gathered from different sources, collated and made available to those who need it in a form that they can use. Large organisations usually establish *computer networks* that are 'powered' by a central computer linked to terminals in each department. Information can then be moved around the system quite freely. Confidentiality and security is safeguarded by the use of *passwords*. People entitled to access sensitive information have to enter the password before they can enter that part of the system – it's the same principle as restricting the number of key holders to a certain filing cabinet.

Information systems are developing rapidly and it is becoming commonplace for organisations to link, via the telephone system, into an international network of computers – called the 'Internet'. They can then communicate faster and cheaper than by letter or fax, and enter into a dialogue. Vast quantities of general information are also available on the Internet that can be accessed by organisations or individuals.

You need to consider how your staff can become 'computer literate'. Promotion and professional development depends increasingly on these information technology skills.

Data and information

There are many types of data used in the health and care sectors:

- patients/clients;
- staff;
- physical resources;
- money;
- community (for example population statistics).

Data storage

Data can be stored in a variety of ways:

- *Human memory* – however sophisticated computer systems might be, we still need to use our brains for storage! People who can absorb and retain important information are highly valued.
- *Paper* – paper-based storage systems can be the most effective and efficient. Many organisations depend almost exclusively on conventional filing systems. They are relatively cheap and, for a small organisation or unit, can be the most cost-effective option. Playgroups, or small- or medium-sized nursing homes, may find that their information

management needs are catered for perfectly well through a paper-based system.

- *Microfiche* – information is transferred from paper to special film (microfiche slides). The advantage is that large amounts of information can be stored on small areas of film. Because of the small print size, special readers are needed to enlarge the text. You may have come across this system in libraries, although it is being rapidly superseded by computer systems.
- *Computer* – data are stored in the computer on disks or on magnetic tape. Normally, tape is only used to make back-up copies. The benefits of computer storage are:
  - large amounts of data can be stored;
  - data can be accessed in different ways for different purposes;
  - data can be accessed quickly and automatically;
  - data are available to large numbers of people at the same time.

Large amounts of information can be stored using computers

A Psion series 3A 'palmtop' computer

A 'multimedia' personal computer of the type frequently found in the home or the home/office

A 'notebook' computer

Large organisations often install networks of computers which can work together but smaller businesses manage with what are known as 'standalone' computers or 'personal computers' (PCs). Many people have become familiar with these at work or at home. A PC can be operated by a single person, will fit on a desktop and provides the four main functions of a computer system – input, output, processing and storage. There are also 'notebook' or 'laptop' computers which, as their names suggest, are small and portable. The *hardware* consists of three basic components:

- A *monitor* (or screen).
- A *keyboard* – similar to a typewriter keyboard and used to put information into the computer and to get data out. A *mouse* (a small, hand-held device) is also used for some of these functions. When you move the mouse, the cursor (a small pointer) moves around the screen.
- A *system unit* – a box which contains microprocessor, memory and disk drives (hard and floppy). The hard disk drive contains a non-removable disk that is built into the computer; it can hold a large amount of information. A floppy disk drive holds a removable floppy disk. This contains less information than a hard disk but it can be removed and used on another compatible machine. Both hard and floppy disks allow data to be entered, changed and read.

Computers have to be told what to do. Sets of instructions are known as *programmes*; collectively, programmes are called *software*.

More recently, PCs can be found with a fourth component – a *CD-ROM* (compact disk – read only memory). This is a form of optical storage, the data being read by laser beam, as in CD players in hi-fi systems. Vast amounts of data can be stored in this way and combined with multimedia systems (for example, sound can be built in).

Information Technology (IT)

The field of IT is vast and it is impossible to summarise its full range. Changes are rapid and you need to keep up-to-date through the professional literature in your area. Take any opportunities you get to participate in staff development activities in IT – they won't be wasted.

There are three major computer-based information technology applications that you need to be aware of:

- *Word processing (WP)* – WP software has revolutionised writing, whether this is in the form of letters, reports or longer pieces. Typewriters have become an endangered species in the Western world. Many managers now use word processing software routinely, even if they can only use the keyboard with two fingers. Text can be corrected, moved and its size or style altered – all before it is printed out.

- *Databases* – using databases, information can be made available across a whole organisation. The benefit is that information is entered once only, can be manipulated in different ways and can be up-dated or accessed by numerous authorised users. Databases are commonly used to handle key information about patients or clients and they come in a variety of different commercial guises. For instance:
  - *Patient Information Systems* containing, perhaps, basic personal and clinical information;
  - *Nurse Information Systems* used, for example, for rostering staff and for care planning;
  - *Stock control systems* which can link usage with orders and stock control.
- *Spreadsheets* – these are used for numerical information, such as budget reports (see Chapter 8). Spreadsheets can automatically update whole calculations when a single number is changed; this saves the time of having to re-calculate from the beginning. For example, you may need to know how much money you have left after every expenditure or every payment into your account. You could set up a spreadsheet to do this for you. Every time you add or deduct an individual amount, the total will change too. Spreadsheets can be linked to other kinds of software, for example databases, to provide a very powerful means of analysing information. Many packages also allow the user to present information in the form of graphs and other types of diagram.

The Data Protection Act 1984

This legislation protects personal information held on computer from misuse. The Access to Health Records Act 1990 (implemented from November 1991) extended this protection to manually-held health records.

Organisations which hold personal data on computer must register with the Data Protection Registrar. People who have personal records held on computer have the right to access this information.

The Data Protection Act regulates:

- the registration of information systems;
- the kind of data that can be held;

ACTIVITY

Examine the information systems you use in your workplace.

- What forms of information storage do you use?
- How effective are they?
- How would you like to improve your present system?
- How would you make the case to your manager for an improvement to the present system?

- who in the organisation has access to information;
- how information can be used;
- the access of individuals to their own records.

You should ensure that you are clear about how these laws apply to your area of work. A very useful publication is the *Guidelines to the Data Protection Act 1984*; details are given at the end of this chapter.

5.4 Marketing the organisation

The effective marketing of services is essential in present day health and social care. The internal market has increased awareness of the principles and practice of marketing. Competition can be intense and the approach to marketing needs to be similar to that seen in the commercial and industrial sectors.

Marketing is much more than publicity and selling:

> 'Marketing is the management process which identifies, anticipates and supplies customer requirements efficiently and profitably.'
>
> The Chartered Institute of Marketing

As you can see from this definition, marketing begins by finding out what the customer wants and then tries to provide it.

Marketing teaches us that:

- the customer is central;
- marketing must be a core activity in any organisation; everyone must play their part;
- success depends on being able to respond to changing needs.

Looked at in this way, the values of care do not need to be in conflict with those of marketing. Both recognise that the individual is central and has changing needs.

Market analysis

Understanding the local market is important for any organisation. There are different ways of analysing your market; one is to undertake a 'SWOT' analysis:

S = strengths
W = weaknesses
O = opportunities
T = threats

For example, a private counselling service might identify the following as part of its market analysis:

Strengths: expert staff
high success rate
Weaknesses: costs of accommodation
weak administrative systems leading to errors in appointments
Opportunities: consultancy for local businesses
diversification into group counselling
Threats: more GPs are employing counsellors
more private counsellors are in the area

Once you have a clearer idea of your own organisation and the local market, it is important to develop a marketing strategy. This should contain objectives, a time scale for their achievement and the estimated costs. An important part of a marketing strategy is to decide on an appropriate *image* for the organisation.

> **ACTIVITY**
>
> Think about your own organisation.
>
> - Carry out a SWOT analysis, identifying as many ideas as possible.
> - Look at the main opportunities you have identified.
> - How would you go about exploiting these opportunities?

Image

Every organisation should be concerned about its image in the community. Excellent work should be widely publicised because, in this way, you can acknowledge the strengths of your staff and the quality of care they provide.

There are many ways in which you can influence the image of your organisation:

- *Name* – notice how many healthcare Trusts have chosen their names to provide a more positive image. For example, a Trust providing care for people with learning difficulties has been called ‘New Possibilities NHS Trust’.
- *Corporate identity* – this includes the use of logos and standard ways of presenting business letters, business cards and so on. It may also involve staff wearing name badges.
- *Buildings and signs* – the external condition of a building conveys strong messages and the state of signboards can demonstrate a sensitivity, or otherwise, to clients’ needs. Bright and attractive reception areas are much more appealing than those which are drab and untidy.
- *Brochures* – these can be costly, especially if printed in full colour. Some organisations produce these without adequate care. The presentation and contents should be tailored to the intended audience. For example, a care home might want to produce a brochure which covers some or all of the following points:

- philosophy and aims of the home;
- location and external appearance;
- local services – such as shops, banks, doctors, cinema, churches, railway and bus stations;
- number of rooms, whether single or shared;
- residents' charter of rights;
- visiting arrangements;
- range of care – for example permanent, respite, day care services;
- special amenities – for example garden, occupational therapy room, music room;
- catering arrangements – menus, dining room or own room;
- policy on pets;
- policy on bringing own furniture;
- policy on smoking and alcohol;
- transport arrangements, such as minibus;
- meeting spiritual needs – details of services;
- staff – qualifications and experience;
- fee structure;
- admission arrangements – trial periods;
- contact names and numbers;
- complaints procedures;
- photographs and diagrams showing facilities and care being given.

Language should be clear, direct and free from jargon. Where the market includes people from ethnic groups whose first language is not English, brochures and other written details should be produced in other relevant languages.

ACTIVITY

How well does your organisation use the local market? Consider this under the following headings:

- Buildings – appearance, signs, etc.
- Brochures, letter heads, etc.
- Local contacts.

Assess how well you are doing by checking what you do against the suggestions made in this chapter.

Keeping in touch with the market

You should build up a list of local contacts who can be kept in touch with developments in your organisation. If possible, produce this on a computer database, where you can up-date it regularly and print it out for reference when necessary. Word of mouth is an important way of publicising what you do. The more local people and organisations who know about how well you are doing, the better your reputation. A short newsletter might be worth considering. Key contacts include:

- local papers, TV and radio – address information to the relevant editors;
- schools, colleges and universities – you can find out about new training opportunities, or offer placements to students needing work experience;
- doctors and other health professionals – for example GPs, consultants, physiotherapists, occupational therapists;
- social services – key managers and registration staff;
- local religious leaders;
- tourist information offices – useful information about local events;
- voluntary groups and organisations;
- local councillors, MPs and MEPs.

Finding out more...

★ The *Guidelines to the Data Protection Act 1984* can be obtained from the Office of the Data Protection Registrar, Springfield House, Water Lane, Wilmslow, SK9 5AX. Tel. 01625 535777.

Reading on ...

★ *British Journal of Healthcare Computing* – this provides up-to-date news and articles about all aspects of computing in health care.
★ *The Penguin Dictionary of English Synonyms and Antonyms* (1992), Penguin, Harmondsworth.
★ Gowers, Sir Ernest (1987) *The Complete Plain Words*, Penguin, Harmondsworth. (Revised by Sidney Greenbaum and Janet Whitcut).
★ *The Oxford Dictionary of English Grammar* (1993), Oxford University Press.
★ *The Oxford Guide to English Usage* (1993), Oxford University Press.
★ Peters, Tom (1989) *Thriving on Chaos*, Macmillan, London.
★ *Roget's Thesaurus*, current edn., Longman, Harlow.
★ Venolia, Janet G. (1991) *Write Right*, David St John Thomas, Nairn.

6 Organising the work

6.1 Planning work

With a systematic approach to your work, you are likely to achieve the results you want. This implies that you need to think carefully about how you plan.

Just to what extent you get involved in planning will depend on your role within the organisation. For example, as a manager in a private nursery with relatively few staff, you may be invited by the proprietor to play a major role in planning overall strategy; you may make decisions about expansion, costing, quality systems, and so on. If you are a nurse leading a team of staff in the out-patient department of an acute health trust, your role may be very different. Top management will decide overall strategy, middle management will interpret it, and you will be responsible for implementing these decisions.

Many organisations encourage an open approach to management which ensures that top managers listen to the views of staff working at all levels. Nevertheless, in large organisations, it is common to feel that decisions are taken at a distance and without adequate consultation. You have a vital role in reducing this sense of powerlessness. You should know the overall goals of the organisation, understand its ambitions and problems, and try to anticipate any changes in policy. By developing an awareness of the 'political' issues, you can put decisions into context and interpret events for your staff. This positive attitude of mind will lift morale and improve performance.

Timescale is important. Much of your planning may be relatively short term, for instance planning for today or the next few days or weeks. Senior managers will take a much longer view, looking ahead to the next few months and years. Care workers too have to plan their own work with clients during a working shift. However, whatever the timescale or scope, you will need to use the same basic set of skills to achieve results.

What does planning involve?

In any plan there are 5 key stages:

- *Stage 1* Set the goal;
- *Stage 2* Assess current strengths and weaknesses;
- *Stage 3* Develop a plan;
- *Stage 4* Put the plan into action;
- *Stage 5* Monitor and evaluate the plan.

Setting goals

Goals are broad statements of outcome. Examples are:

- To negotiate a social activity programme with clients;
- To ensure that patients have sufficient opportunity to express their views about the care they have received;
- To introduce a key worker system.

The last example will be used to illustrate the other stages. To make progress with these goals, you should break them down into smaller steps.

Assessing strengths and weaknesses

You need to know enough about the present situation before detailed plans can be made.

> *Example*
> Overall staff numbers are probably satisfactory but the level of morale is low and turnover high. Quality of care is adequate but not improving. You have one member of staff who has experience of the key worker system from a previous job. There are no locally organised training courses covering the key worker approach. There is strong commitment from top management for the key worker system but very little extra money – £1000.00 has been allocated for start-up training.

Developing a plan

Within the overall goal and with knowledge of existing strengths and weaknesses, you can set out detailed plans.

> *Example*
> Introduce the organisation's goal to your staff; ask for their ideas.
> Talk to the client committee to explain the system and ask for their ideas.
> Develop an in-house training programme.
> Ask a small group of staff to survey the journals for articles about key working, and to prepare a summary.
> Discuss quality measures with top management to see if the effectiveness of the proposed key worker system can be measured.
> Introduce the key worker system on a pilot basis within two months.
> Prepare a Gantt chart.

GANTT CHART

Many people find planning easier if they use visual aids to track progress of a project. The Gantt chart is one of the best methods of doing this and can be made as simple or as complicated as you wish. The basic idea is to set out visually the activities which need to occur and when they should happen. Here is a simple Gantt chart for the key worker example:

GANTT CHART								
Goal: To introduce a key worker system								
	JAN	FEB	MAR	APR	MAY	JUN	JUL	AUG
Initial discussions with team	***********							
Monitoring meetings with team		************	************	************	************	************	************	
Gather information about key worker system	*****	************						
Discuss idea with client committee		************						
Discuss quality issues with manager			*****					
Decide on pilot arrangements			*****					
Pilot running				************	************	************	************	
External training event			*****					
Visit to other units				*****	*****			
Fortnightly updates				*****	************	************	************	
Weekly reviews with supervisor				************	************	************	************	
Evaluate initial phase of programme							************	

Putting the plan into action

This is the implementation stage. Ensure all staff know what is happening.

> *Example:*
> Arrange for an external trainer to run an intensive two-day workshop on key working.
> Arrange for a group of staff to visit another unit where the system has been operating for some years; ask for client representation on this visit.
> Write a fortnightly 'update' to tell the team and other staff in the organisation what is going on.

Monitoring and evaluating the plan

Effective monitoring and evaluation will pick up problems early and allow you to take corrective action. You need to establish a feedback system to give you the information you need.

Example
Review the progress of the plan on a weekly basis with your own supervisor. The idea to pilot the key worker system has been heavily criticised – most staff believe that it would be better to introduce a simplified system across the board; this idea is confirmed by the visit.

6.2 Organising staff

You must organise your staff in ways which meet the needs of clients and are acceptable to your managers and staff. What might at first glance seem a very efficient method of working may not always be so in practice. For example, it used to be common practice for nurses to undertake specific tasks, such as taking temperatures or giving baths, for all patients in a ward – this is known as 'task-centred care'. Gradually, the importance of the nurse–patient relationship began to emerge and task-centred care gradually gave way to 'patient-centred care' in which nurses have responsibility for the complete care of a group of patients.

Methods of organising care staff

Methods of organising care staff should:

- meet the individual needs of the client – in other words they should be 'client-centred';
- value the quality of the relationship between client and care worker;
- recognise that individual care workers are accountable for their actions;
- encourage flexibility;
- encourage team work.

You can encourage greater accountability by adopting the key worker system. A key worker coordinates the care of a group of clients, liaising with other professionals and maintaining care plans. In nursing, the *primary nurse* carries out a similar role.

These approaches have several potential benefits:

- clients know who is responsible for their care; they have an individual member of staff to turn to for information or practical help;
- trust can develop more easily between client and care worker;
- other care workers know who to contact about the care of a particular client.

The principles are straightforward, the practices more complex. You need to be aware of the possible difficulties in implementing these systems, for example:

- key workers cannot be available at all times; other members of the team have to take on the care of the client when the designated person is off duty;
- care documentation needs to be clear and usable by all staff;
- care workers need sufficient authority to organise care and need to know who to refer problems to;
- care workers must have adequate experience to carry out these roles effectively – this has implications for staff salary gradings.

ACTIVITY

Consider the following questions:

- What care system is used in your own place of work?
- Is it suited to the needs of clients and staff?
- How could it be improved?

Motivating staff

Motivating your staff and maintaining high morale should be key objectives. To achieve these, you should:

- give clear definitions of tasks and objectives; clarify expectations and make sure that staff understand the targets to be met;
- give quick, accurate and sufficient feedback on staff performance;
- establish clear lines of responsibility and accountability, and clear systems of reporting and recording;
- provide adequate support systems, such as supervision, training and staff development opportunities.
- respect individual team members' needs for autonomy;
- encourage participation in decision-making and implementation;
- don't expect members of staff to carry responsibilities beyond their levels of competence.

Delegating tasks

Effective management cannot take place without adequate delegation of tasks. However, you should always remember to delegate sufficient authority to accomplish the task. Some managers find it hard to delegate at all. Others do so but without adequate preparation or subsequent monitoring.

The aims of delegation are to:

- push decision-making down the hierarchy as far as possible so that actions are taken where they are most relevant by the people who are most involved;
- free the delegator to do higher-level work;
- provide experience for the member of staff to whom work has been delegated; monitoring and control should accompany delegation.

ACTIVITY

Consider the following situation:
Martin is a senior staff nurse in an acute surgical ward. Following the results of a survey carried out by the Trust's customer services unit, his manager has asked him to set up a support group for the relatives of patients who have undergone facial surgery. This is the first major task that the manager has delegated to Martin.

However, after several weeks Martin has made little progress. He cannot organise a suitable room because those responsible for central resources don't return his phone calls, the catering manager seems reluctant to provide tea and coffee and his colleagues feel he should be getting on with his 'real work'.

- What is going wrong?
- How could these problems have been avoided?
- How would you now try to put this situation right?

6.3 Decision-making skills

Decisions involve choices. Sometimes the options are clear and straightforward; at other times, the options are vague and difficult. Often you will have to make decisions under tricky conditions – for example when you don't have all the facts, or when you are unsure about the intended outcome. Every decision also involves some risk – especially in the care sector where vulnerable people are the targets of decision-making.

> **ACTIVITY**
>
> Consider the following situations:
>
> *A* Sally, a senior care assistant in a home for people with learning difficulties, has been asked by a member of her team how she should deal with John, one of the residents. He has asked if he can go out and buy a radio-cassette player. The philosophy of the home stresses individual choice and independence. Although John might find using the controls difficult at first, there are no other problems with such a purchase. Finance is not a problem because John has saved enough money.
>
> *B* On another occasion, Sally is told by one of her team that the cleaner has been overheard asking a resident for money. After some thought, Sally decides that she should speak at once to the cleaner concerned and confront her with this accusation. The cleaner is outraged, saying that the whole thing was a light-hearted comment and that care staff should have better things to do than stand around listening in to other peoples' conversations.
>
> - If you were in Sally's position which situation would you find it easiest to deal with?
> - In each case, what factors should Sally consider when coming to a decision?
> - What would be your decision in each case?

Styles and approaches

Although everyone will approach decision-making in different ways, we can identify four broad approaches:

Consultative

If you adopt a consultative approach to decision-making, you seek the views of others as to the best course of action. The responsibility for the final decision is yours but you believe that the best decision cannot be made without listening to the opinions of others. Who you consult will depend on the type of decision and who will be affected by the outcome.

The time-scale for a decision may not allow you to consult as widely as you would like. Consulting too many people will be unnecessary and take too much time; if you do not consult widely enough, your decision may be too subjective. Decide who are the key people for any particular decision and stick to this group.

DECISION STEPS

1 Recognise the problem;
2 Is this my problem?
3 Consider the alternatives;
4 Collect information;
5 Evaluate the alternatives;
6 Make and implement the decision;
7 Follow up your decision.

1 Recognise the problem

Problems are of many types, such as variations between what is expected and what actually happens; tensions arising between staff; underperformance of a team member; choices due to resource constraints; high levels of complaints from clients.

2 Is this my problem?

In the course of your work, you will meet all sorts of problems: some will be your responsibility, others will not. Muddle and conflict can occur if you stray too far from your own area of responsibility. If the problem is yours, define it as carefully as you can. Make sure you are addressing the real problem, not just the symptoms.

3 Consider the alternatives

You will only be able to find an appropriate solution if you have enough alternatives. Brainstorming is a useful technique for getting ideas (see later in this chapter).

ACTIVITY

You are trying to decide on a holiday destination for a group of clients. With the help of your staff, you draw up the following list of criteria:

- cost – travel, accommodation;
- distance and travelling time;
- availability of local support in a crisis;
- wishes of clients;
- available staff – numbers and experience;
- numbers of clients wishing to go;
- range of appropriate activities available locally;
- the need for a pre-visit by staff.

Put these criteria in priority order; alternatively, rate each of them as top, middle or low priority.

4 Collect information

You need to collect evidence about possible alternatives. How much you can collect will depend on your resources – time, money, availability, access to experts. Good evidence allows you to be as objective as possible. The sort of information you might want includes: acceptability (to clients or colleagues), relative costs, impact on other services, whether the solution is likely to be short, medium or long term.

5 Evaluate the alternatives

You should weigh up the alternatives in the light of the information collected. Where possible establish criteria for making a final decision. Clear criteria help you to make decisions more objectively.

6 Make and implement the decision

Make up your mind, tell the staff concerned and explain why. Not all your decisions will be the right ones, but often you will only know this with hindsight. Don't be indecisive. Staff can become frustrated and demotivated if their team leader is seen as too tentative.

7 Follow up your decision

You also need to set out the ways in which you can judge (evaluate) whether the decision has been effective. With the holiday example given in the activity, you can evaluate fairly soon but with other decisions, such as the purchase of a new piece of equipment for a physiotherapy department, it may be months or years before its true worth becomes apparent.

Creative techniques for decision-making

Making decisions is one of the most taxing yet exciting aspects of your role as a manager. Taxing because it is the clearest expression of your responsibilities and you want to get it right; exciting because every decision, however straightforward it may seem at first sight, contains an element of risk.

There are various practical ways of coping with decision-making. Compare your own techniques with those summarised here – you might want to try some.

Plan thinking time

Build in some thinking time for yourself in the course of your working day. Protect your official break times as far as you can; it can be all too easy to allow the work to slide into what should be your own time. It's unavoidable occasionally but the quality of your managerial skills will decline if you allow work to encroach consistently on your personal time, and your decisions will suffer in the long run.

Set a deadline for yourself

You will often be working to a deadline imposed by others but, if not, set one for yourself. Letting things drift will not improve the final decision.

Change your environment

Get away from your usual work environment. Go for a walk or go to a library and browse in unfamiliar territory. The break in routine will often spark different ways of thinking about problems.

Brainstorming

This is usually done in groups, although some people also find it useful on their own; the aim is to generate as many different solutions as possible to a particular problem. Every idea is accepted without comment, however irrelevant it might seem at first glance. If you are leading this activity, encourage the group to produce as many ideas as possible without any attempt to censor or discuss them. Most people quickly get used to the technique. Record the ideas on a white board, flip chart or just a piece of paper – it works best when the ideas are visible to everyone. When the group has run out of ideas, consider each suggestion in turn until you produce a shortlist of viable options.

Draw pictures and diagrams

Some people think more creatively through pictures; there are similarities with 'mind-mapping' techniques used in study skills courses (see, for

Brainstorming

example, the book by Tony Buzan). By allowing yourself to be 'untidy' on paper, you can often release ideas that might otherwise stay hidden. The strength of these methods is that they let you see new links between ideas.

Don't lose good ideas

Good ideas often appear at the most inconvenient moments: record these when they occur – in the garden, in the bath, in bed, in the car, wherever.

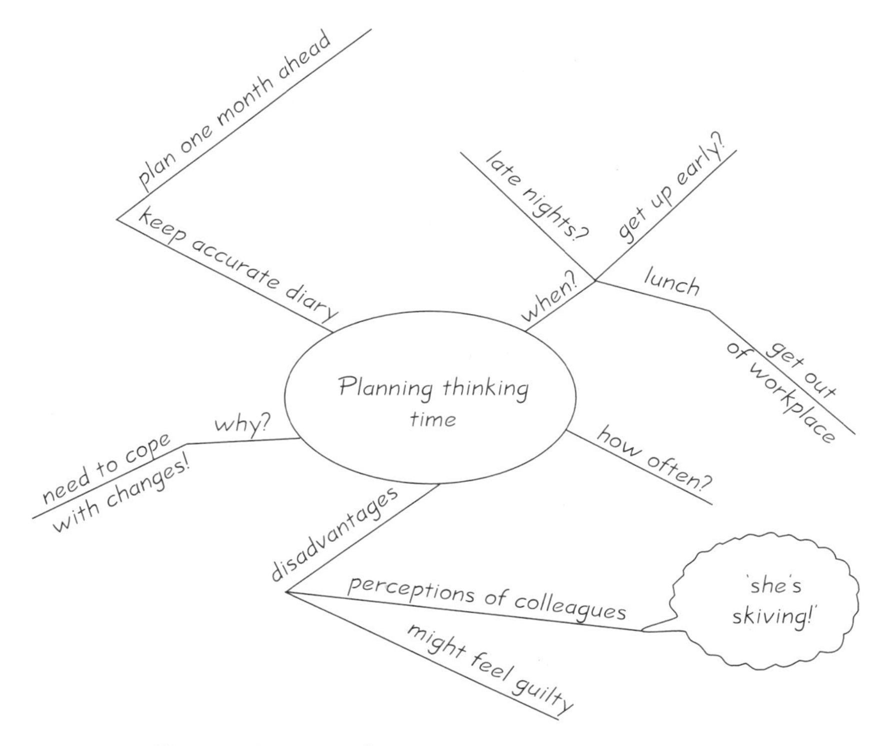

Express yourself creatively – a mind map

Keep a notebook handy. Invest in a pocket tape recorder (microcassette recorder), the only safe way to record ideas while driving!

Relax

This can be anything from a few minutes calm created in the course of a busy day to more complex relaxation methods which need special training. By finding ways of reducing your tensions, you will be in better shape to make sensible decisions.

Look after yourself

Making decisions is stressful, not always unpleasantly so, but you do need to ensure you have a social life and outside interests. Many people who work in the care field take their work home with them to a damaging extent. There is more about this in Chapter 11.

6.4 Time management

The way you spend your time is critical to your effectiveness as a manager. Notice the word 'spend'. The use of time, like any other resource, has a cost.

> **ACTIVITY**
>
> Do you know the cost per hour when a member of your team carries out care activities with clients? Do you know how much it costs for you to attend a meeting? If not, ask your manager or the finance department.

Improving your time management

Most of us could spend our time more effectively if we stopped using our time for such things as:

- correcting mistakes which could have been sorted out the first time round;
- doing things that are interesting to us but less important to our employer;
- doing things that others should be doing;
- applying standards of work that are unnecessarily high;
- avoiding using time-saving equipment, such as word processors.

Here are some tips for improving your time management:

1 Decide what it is you want to do each day (or week). One way of achieving this is to draw up a list of 'things to do';
   - List everything you have to do;
   - Put these in order of priority;
   - Decide which tasks you have to do personally and which can be delegated.

   Modify this list during the day (or week) to cope with emergencies but don't lose track of important tasks. Defer some if you need to but always put them in the diary for later.

2 Keep your desk or work area in order. Try these ideas:
   - Don't allow your desk to reach 'crisis point'. When you are at your wits end, gather together all the clutter into *one heap*. You may then be able to work through the pile with greater composure.
   - There is a school of thought which maintains that *pending trays* are unnecessary. Perhaps. I have used the 'pending' facility throughout

> **ACTIVITY**
>
> How well do you think you use your own time? How well do you think others use their time? Draw up three lists:
>
> - ways in which you waste the time of others;
> - ways in which your manager wastes your time;
> - ways in which your staff waste their time.

my career. However, I have learnt the lesson that pending does not mean indefinite. Go through your pending tray frequently and dispose of everything which has become irrelevant. For many people, this means simply removing the bottom half inch!

- Choose a time in the week to *tidy up* your desk or work area. If nothing else, this will give you time to think and thinking time is often the most valuable of all.

3 Keep your own meetings strictly to time. If you are attending someone else's meeting, make it clear to the chairperson at or before the start if you need to leave at a particular time: this avoids you wasting your time while showing respect for the chairperson.

4 If you feel overwhelmed by the number of things you have to do:
- decide on a priority order according to when deadlines have to be met;
- when you can, choose a priority task which can be completed quickly; this gets you off to a good start by giving you an early sense of achievement.

5 Communicate as clearly as possible. For example, ensure your memos and messages are conveyed concisely and precisely. Avoid too much 'thinking out loud' with colleagues – think first, communicate second!

6 Make time management part of your personal agenda when you have supervision with your own manager.

ACTIVITY

It can be difficult to assess your own time management skills. Get a colleague to observe you in the course of your everyday work. Arrange to discuss this after a set time, say two weeks. Offer to do the same for your colleague. Peer evaluation of this sort is useful and can build trust across teams.

ACTIVITY

You have a responsibility to give your staff the chance to get on with their work – to make the best use of their time. Ask yourself these questions:

- Do I achieve a sensible balance between face-to-face management and 'standing back' and allowing staff to get on with the job?
- Do any of my staff ever suggest that I am 'interfering' in their work?

Reading on...

★ Buzan, Tony (1995) *Use Your Head*, BBC Publications, London. An entertaining and instructive book setting out the techniques of 'mind mapping'.

★ Catt, Stephen E. and Miller, Donald S. (1991) *Supervision: working with people*, Irwin, Boston.

7 Giving the best quality care

One of your main tasks is to improve the quality of care in your area of work. This is no easy task. Quality of care is difficult to define and trying to achieve it is not the same thing as actually achieving it.

Influences outside your immediate work situation will often determine the level of quality you are able to provide. For example, limited resources will almost always frustrate your ideals. You may work in an organisation where senior managers make all key decisions about controlling quality and setting standards. However, by getting to grips with the topics in this chapter, you can ensure that you contribute informed opinions at work and implement senior management decisions with conviction.

Most importantly, you should aim to work with your staff to create an atmosphere in which the main goal is to improve quality for the client. As a result, you will find that staff morale, job satisfaction and client care all benefit.

Historically, the manufacturing industries devised the first systematic methods of quality control. During the 1980s, the government developed health and social care policies rooted firmly in market forces which emphasised the value of competition. As a result, it was no surprise when the practices associated with industry and commerce were introduced into the public sector. *Quality assurance* was one of these practices.

In the NHS, health authorities and fund-holding general practices influence the quality of care through the specifications that they write into their contracts with providers, such as NHS Trusts. These specifications cover what and how much is to be provided, at what price and at what level of quality. Purchasers may base their quality specifications on recognised theory, for example some use the Maxwell dimensions as a framework (this is discussed later in this chapter).

In social services departments, inspection services have become 'arms length', that is they have been reorganised in order to separate the inspectors from the providers of care. For example, all inspections of care, nursing homes and nurseries (public, private and voluntary) are carried out by a special inspection unit of the social services department.

Public, private and voluntary sector organisations are beginning to state openly what they can offer and how 'customers' can complain when things go wrong. Many large organisations now have their own charters (see Chapter 3).

Clients (or 'patients', 'customers' or 'users' depending on where you work) have become much better educated about their rights. To a large extent, this has been due to the mass media – television, radio, newspapers and magazines frequently include features about consumer rights. Social service departments, NHS Trusts and private and voluntary sector organisations publish their own complaints procedures and these have also been important

ACTIVITY

In what ways would you like to improve quality in your workplace? If you can, discuss this with colleagues and with your team. Draw up a list of priority areas. Here is an example of a list produced by a manager in a day care unit:

1 the initial assessment of clients;
2 liaison with transport services;
3 communications within the unit;
4 care documentation.

Keep your list in mind as you read through this section and try to develop practical ideas for making improvements.

in raising awareness. The end result is that more people are willing to complain when standards aren't up to scratch.

Despite these changes, many people using health and social care services remain rather reluctant to complain directly about their own care or that provided for their relatives. Some vulnerable clients are unable to do this because of physical or psychological limitations. This applies especially to children, older people and people with learning disabilities or mental health problems. If you work in these fields, you will need to be creative in giving a proper voice to these clients. There are some suggestions for you later in this section (see Client Satisfaction, page 74).

USEFUL DEFINITIONS

Audit The sharing by a group of peers of information gained from personal experience and/or care records in order to assess and improve the care provided for their clients/patients. It focuses on the performance of individual practitioners and the service provided to individual clients/patients.

Criterion (plural = criteria) A component or aspect of a care system which indicates the quality of the care provided; for example the ratio of carers to clients, the training of staff, the amount of time spent talking to clients each day.

Quality assessment The measurement of the care provided against expectations.

Quality assurance The processes of measuring how well the care provided meets expectations and the prevention, prediction and correction of any deficiencies.

Standard An agreed level of performance in relation to a criterion; for example there will always be at least three carers on duty; the training needs of each member of staff will be assessed annually; every client will receive each day a minimum of 30 minutes uninterrupted one-to-one conversation with a carer.

Total quality management An all embracing approach to quality assurance which is based on total commitment from the whole organisation; a wide range of specific quality improvement methods is used.

7.1 Approaches to quality

Quality is not a commodity that can be purchased off-the-shelf like a tin of baked beans nor, indeed, is it a philosophy that can be absorbed in one go. It is a long-term commitment. As Philip Crosby has put it, quality management requires 'unblinking dedication, patience and time' (Crosby 1993).

There are many definitions of quality, each of which has its particular strengths and weaknesses. The *Department of Trade and Industry* has said that:

> 'quality means giving complete satisfaction – providing customers with exactly what they want, when they want it, at a price they can afford.'
>
> Department of Trade and Industry 1990

However, what does 'complete satisfaction' actually mean? If I can buy an affordable, well-fitting pair of shoes whenever I want to, then perhaps that is complete satisfaction. But what of the older person who is mentally confused, has a leg ulcer, needs care now and yet there is no bed available? From this example, it is clear that health and social care presents us with complex and difficult situations where quality is going to be problematic. Adopting the DTI definition without qualification would raise the question of whether quality care could ever be achieved.

Philip Crosby, a well known American management consultant who writes prolifically on quality, says that, if we are going to be able to manage quality, it needs to be defined as 'conformance to requirements' (Crosby 1993). This may sound uninspiring but has the advantages of both practicability and realism. To achieve quality, you must ensure that you carry out your tasks according to what is required. This implies that you need to work to clear standards and instructions.

Crosby invented several pithy statements that have become widely quoted. For example:

> 'Right first time, every time'
> 'Zero defects'

The reason for this advice is that correcting mistakes is expensive. Think of how annoying it is to have to put right an error – whether someone else's or your own. You have to apologise and you have to sort out the problem – much easier to have got it right the first time.

There are parts of any organisation which seem, routinely, to make fewer errors than others. Philip Crosby uses the pay-roll department as a prime example. Because staff won't tolerate errors in their pay, the pay-roll department in most organisations works to a very high standard indeed! Crosby's view is that 'zero defects' (in other words no mistakes) is a standard that management should expect in all parts of an organisation.

ACTIVITY

Think about Crosby's ideas of 'conformance to requirements' and 'zero defects'.

- Do you always know what the 'requirements' are in your job?
- Identify the areas in your work
  (a) where you are clear about the requirements
  (b) where you are less certain.
- How often do you find yourself having to correct the mistakes of others?
- How often do you make a preventable mistake yourself?
- What would you need to be able to prevent these errors? More resources? More attention on your own part? Or more cooperation from your staff, or from the senior management?

One of the most influential writers about quality in the health service is *John Øvretveit*. His definition of quality is:

> 'Fully meeting the needs of those who need the service most, at the lowest cost to the organisation, within limits and directives set by higher authorities.'
> Øvretveit 1992

He divides quality into three dimensions:

- *Client quality* is what the clients think about a service. As a manager, your role is how to increase their satisfaction and reduce their dissatisfaction.
- *Professional quality* comprises the judgements made by the professionals on whether a service meets the needs of clients and whether the practice is up to standard.
- *Management quality* is selecting and deploying resources 'in the most efficient way to meet customer needs, within limits and directives' (Øvretveit, 1992).

Like Crosby's, this definition recognises that quality care always has to operate 'within limits'. It also explicitly mentions the need to keep costs as low as possible. Quality improvements have to pay their way.

How do you define who needs the service most? More importantly, who defines this? If limits were to continue to be tightened, for example by continuously falling budgets, would standards fall so much that the very idea of quality seemed meaningless?

There are other, more subjective, interpretations of quality that are worth reflecting on. *Alison Kitson* is a nurse who has done a great deal to promote standard-setting in the health service. She warns us against adopting a mechanistic view of quality. At all times, we need to be aware of the individual client at the centre of the whole process. As she puts it, quality is to do with 'fostering a sense of the individual within a system' (Kitson, 1987). The ability to meet the needs of another person depends upon a meeting of minds and hearts. Sometimes this means that you have to trust your intuitions and gut reactions. In the rush to implement the latest off-the-shelf quality technique, you can easily overlook this more personal side.

Avedis Donabedian is a major international figure in the quality field as it applies to health care. His ideas have been adopted widely by many professions and have influenced the development of quality systems worldwide. You may find his framework helpful in setting standards. He identifies three groups of factors which influence quality:

- *Structure* – 'the physical, organisational and other characteristics of the system that provides care and of its environment'. For example, this includes the premises, budget, policies and procedures and skill mix.
- *Process* – 'what is done in caring for patients'. This refers to how the care operates in practice.
- *Outcome* – 'what is achieved, an improvement usually in health but also in attitudes, knowledge, and behaviour conducive to future health' (Donabedian 1986). Typical outcomes are discharge rates, client satisfaction survey results, and attitude changes due to a health promotion campaign, as well as specific outcomes you might write into care plans for individual clients.

In 1984, *R.J. Maxwell* wrote an article on 'Quality assessment in health' which proposed that quality in the care field should take into account six different dimensions. These are shown in the Box on page 70. What is particularly useful about Maxwell's ideas is that they provide us with a means of making judgements about quality. Since the dimensions were first published, many other writers in the quality field, and many purchasing authorities too, have made use of them – a sure sign of their practical value.

THE SIX DIMENSIONS OF QUALITY (based on Maxwell, 1984)

Appropriateness The service is appropriate when it is what clients actually need.
Equity The service is equitable when all clients receive their fair share of care.
Accessibility For example, services are accessible when waiting lists are not too long or when clients do not have to travel excessive distances to receive care.
Effectiveness A service is effective when it achieves the intended benefit for clients.
Acceptability Services are acceptable when they satisfy the reasonable expectations of clients, providers and the community.
Efficiency Services are efficient when resources are not wasted on one service or client to the detriment of another.

ACTIVITY

Apply Maxwell's ideas to your own area of work by using the grid below. I have selected three aspects of care as examples. You might want to substitute or add others. Assess each aspect of care by rating it in terms of the six dimensions, using the following scale:

3 – strongly achieved;
2 – satisfactorily achieved;
1 – not achieved to a satisfactory level.

	Appropriate-ness	Equity	Access-ibility	Effective-ness	Accept-ability	Efficiency
Psycho-logical care	3	1	1	2	1	2
Staff training						
Support for relatives						

To show how you might do this, I have completed the first line – psychological care. Imagine that you have completed this as the manager of an acute medical ward.

Appropriateness: rated 3 because many of your patients do have psychological needs, such as problems adapting to the fact of a heart attack.
Equity: rated 1 because, although psychological care is appropriate, you can only meet these needs for *some* of your patients.
Accessibility: rated 1 because there is never enough time and you are short of appropriately trained counselling staff.
Effectiveness: rated 2 because clients who do receive this care benefit from it to a satisfactory level.
Acceptability: rated 1 because there is inadequate privacy for individual counselling and clients and their relatives have complained about this.
Efficiency: rated 2 because, generally, you select the clients with the most pressing needs and therefore the resources could not have been used better.

7.2 How to improve quality of care

Many of your staff will have considerable experience in providing care. You should take advantage of this by listening very carefully to their views about what makes for good quality. If you neglect to take existing expertise and experience into account, you will be inviting failure. Quality improvements depend upon the effective management of change, and direct carers need to be well motivated, involved and convinced of the value of change. As a major link between senior management and direct care staff, you have a key role to play in this process.

How can you motivate your staff to develop a commitment to quality? Here are a few suggestions:

- demonstrate your own commitment by integrating quality considerations into all aspects of your work, for example by examining your own performance and reducing errors;
- ensure that all staff are clear about the requirements of their jobs, including those that relate to quality itself;
- work hard to create a team spirit that values quality and encourages reflection and questioning, that takes nothing for granted;
- organise regular meetings where you can discuss frankly how well the team is doing, including your own performance.

There are several organisation-wide approaches to quality. These include:

Total Quality Management (TQM)

There is no single correct way to implement TQM but the general principles are that:

- *the whole organisation is involved* – every employee involved from the chief executive to the most recently-employed care assistant; all systems are involved, for example direct patient care, reception, waste disposal;
- *the process is permanent* – it is not a short-term solution;
- *the needs of the customer must be understood* – not just outside customers – everyone in the organisation is both a customer (receives a service) and a supplier (supplies a service); this approach stresses commitment to quality throughout the working day;
- *quality has to be managed* – it will not happen spontaneously.

BS EN ISO 9000 (formerly known as BS 5750)

The British Standards Institution (BSI) sets out standards for all kinds of products and services. In 1979, the BSI introduced BS 5750, a standard for quality systems in all organisations, whatever their size or business. By 1991, more than 12 000 organisations had been assessed and registered. An increasing number of health and social care organisations have used BS 5750 as a springboard for improving the quality of their work – from small care homes to NHS Trusts. BSI Inspectors visit regularly to check the implementation of the organisation's compliance with BS 5750. In 1994, BS 5750 was revised and given a new number – BS EN ISO 9000.

As the DTI put it, BS 5750:

> 'sets out how you can establish, document and maintain an effective quality system which will demonstrate to your customers that you are committed to quality and are able to supply their quality needs.'

Investors in People (IIP)

This is a government initiative managed through the Training and Enterprise Councils (TECs). It focuses on staff training and development. Many organisations in the care sector have supported IIP perhaps because the philosophy is very much in tune with care values, such as promoting individual potential. There are four sections to IIP:

1. *Commitment* An Investor in People makes a public commitment from the top to develop all employees to achieve its business objectives.
2. *Planning* An Investor in People regularly reviews the training and development needs of all employees.
3. *Action* An Investor in People takes action to train and develop individuals on recruitment and throughout their employment.
4. *Evaluation* An Investor in People evaluates the investment in training and development to assess achievement and improve future effectiveness.

Standard Setting

Care organisations commonly use methods of standard setting to monitor and improve quality. Without explicit standards, you will be unable to judge accurately whether a service is meeting its objectives.

Øvretveit defines a standard as:

> '...a specific expectation of staff, described in terms of an activity or outcome against which their actions can be measured. The expectation is specified in terms of a level of performance to be achieved on a defined measure or indicator.'
>
> Øvretveit 1992

Sources of standards can be external or internal to the workplace. For example, The United Kingdom Central Council for Nursing, Midwifery and Health Visiting (UKCC) has published standards for the administration of medicines (UKCC, 1992). All registered nurses are bound by these standards because they are accountable individually for their professional practice and the UKCC is the body which maintains the register. Other professions have also produced standards to guide practice.

In the social care sector, Registration Officers use standards to assess the quality of care homes. Their sources include standards published by the Social Service Inspectorate and documents produced by local social services departments.

Internally-produced standards are those written by staff teams themselves. Standards should be written by a group representing the interests of all those involved – staff and, where appropriate, clients. In this way, you will increase relevance, realism and a sense of ownership.

Effective standards are:

- *specific, clear and understandable* – woolly thinking and language will create muddle and demoralisation;
- *measurable* – without this, no corrective action can be taken; the level to be achieved should be established when the standard is first written;
- *achievable* – standards that are too high reduce motivation;
- *relevant* – concerned with an area of care which is important;
- *grammatical* – with a subject, verb and an object;
- *theoretically sound* – based on research, professional guidance, legal requirements.

Many people write standards using the Donabedian framework of structure, process and outcome. Here is an example from occupational therapy. It consists of a 'standard statement', followed by samples of criteria and outcomes.

Standard Statement The occupational therapist will ensure that all older people attending the Royal Oak Day Centre who live at home and who are new clients will have a monthly home visit for the first six months to ensure continuity between the day centre staff and relatives.

Structure

1 The occupational therapist will have access to the client's records.
2 The occupational therapist will have access to other members of staff to discuss changing needs.
3 The occupational therapist will have appropriate transport to undertake the visit.
4 The occupational therapist will contact relatives to make arrangements for visits.

Process

1 The occupational therapist will discuss the client's needs with relatives in the following areas:
   - mobility
   - hygiene
   - communication
   - nutrition
   - any others as indicated by assessments.
2 The occupational therapist will provide advice in these areas.
3 The occupational therapist will discuss the statutory and non-statutory services available.
4 The occupational therapist will record visits in line with local policy.

Outcome

1 Each older person attending the Royal Oak Day Centre for the first time will receive a monthly visit from the occupational therapist for the first six months.
2 Relatives will understand what the occupational therapist is aiming to achieve and will be able to support this in the home.
3 The relatives will have access to specialist advice and guidance from the occupational therapist.
4 Members of the multidisciplinary team will receive regular reports from the occupational therapist about the progress of individual clients.

As a manager, you have the responsibility for:

- ensuring that the standards are consistent with the organisation's stated philosophy, mission statement and strategic goals (where standards threaten to deviate from these, it may be that the philosophy should be reviewed);
- making adequate time available for staff to develop and monitor standards;
- supporting and/or providing training;
- ensuring that standards reflect best practice;
- providing resources – space, equipment, clerical support;
- pacing the process – early enthusiasm can quickly convert into cynicism when progress begins to slow down; encourage staff to see standard setting as part of their everyday responsibilities, not as a one-month wonder;
- praising the effort put in by staff and users – the quality of standard writing will improve with experience and practice but all movement in the right direction should be encouraged.

Auditing

There is little use in writing and agreeing standards if they are not then measured in practice. Auditing is a common method and an audit tool should be designed at the same time as the standard is written. Audit tools include:

- *peer review* – evaluation by colleagues, using rating scales, observation or questionnaires;
- *document audit* – the systematic checking of written records;
- *client satisfaction surveys* – systematically finding out what clients think about their care.

You need to decide

- *WHO* will audit
- *HOW* it will be carried out
- *WHEN* it will happen
- *WHAT* action will follow.

For example:

Standard: 'Each client will have a care plan in which all goals are client-centred.'
Audit: Supervisor to spot check care plans once a week. Supervisor to record audit results on official document and discuss findings with staff at the following team meeting.

Quality circles

A quality circle is defined by Robson as:

> 'a group of 4–10 volunteers working for the same supervisor... who meet once a week , for an hour, under the leadership of the supervisor, to identify, analyse and solve their own work-related problems.'
>
> Robson 1988

This definition does not hold for every quality circle but it gives the general idea. They have been used widely by the health and social services, possibly because both services are already based on team work. You may need to vary the membership of a quality circle, for example by including staff from other departments (either as permanent or ad hoc members).

To keep motivation high, they should be run in a business-like manner with starting and finishing times adhered to. The strengths of quality circles are that they:

- encourage the team members to take responsibility for solving their own problems;
- harness the good ideas and creativity of team members;
- facilitate staff development and motivation.

Management is expected to support the process discreetly by:

- providing resources for the meetings;
- acting on any proposals made by the circle where this is possible; where recommendations cannot be implemented, management must explain why.

Client satisfaction

You will remember that Øvretveit proposed 'client quality' as a central part of his approach to quality assurance. However, he also pointed out that the identity of the client is often complex – it could be the individual patient or it might be a major purchaser of a service (for example a health authority or fund-holding GP practice). Historically, private sector institutions have taken greater interest in customer satisfaction and 'customer care' than public sector organisations, probably because in this sector clients often pay directly for the services they receive.

Always try to establish what your clients think of your service. Don't limit yourself to the immediate clients but include relatives and other visitors and contacts, such as other professionals (social workers, nurses, GPs, health visitors, etc.).

You can choose from many different techniques, including:

- *questionnaires* – these can be simple or complex; they need to be simple enough to encourage people to complete them. Depending on the context, they can be used while clients are receiving care, at the point of discharge or after they have returned to their everyday lives.
- *complaints boxes and books* – ensure these are easily available to clients;
- *suggestion boxes or books* – again they must be accessible;
- *interviews* – with a sample of clients, preferably carried out by a person not involved in the care of these clients; some organisations use telephone interviews to follow-up discharged patients.

If your clients have communication problems or learning disabilities, you will have to find acceptable means to offer them the chance to comment. Here are some ideas you might like to think about:

- invite outside people to act as advocates for clients; relevant voluntary organisations will usually be able to give advice on this and sometimes arrange for people to act as advocates;
- hold informal discussion groups with clients who are unable to write their comments;
- involve relatives by asking them for their opinions;
- try to use more than one method if you can, because this will help to make your results more valid.

ACTIVITY

Arrange a series of three or four 1-hour meetings with your team to discuss the ideas and techniques described in this chapter. It is important to provide an open climate for discussion because the theory is sometimes initially difficult to grasp. The theme of the sessions should be 'How can we improve what we do?' Ideas from the team should be welcomed and accepted for further discussion. Resist the temptation to reject any too quickly. If you do, staff may be reluctant to share their thoughts later.

Towards the end of the series of meetings, draw up an action plan showing how you are going to implement the various quality improvements you have agreed. This could be prepared as a Gantt chart (see Chapter 6).

Assessing client satisfaction

7.3 Maintaining a safe and healthy environment

A safe working environment is the most fundamental requirement for quality. The laws and regulations on health and safety are complex and extensive. This section outlines the main features of legislation and highlights your role as a manager. You can keep up-to-date by regularly requesting information from government bodies and other organisations; details are given at the end of this section.

Care workers are subject to a vast range of potentially harmful situations, practices and physical environments. Because of this, you need to make health and safety one of your highest priorities.

Sources of legislation

The main sources are:

1 *European Union Directives* – EU countries have to implement these, normally within two years of draft publication.
2 *Act of Parliament* – prior to 1974, detailed laws were passed covering specific industries, for example mining, shops and offices. Outside these specific areas workers were not protected.
3 *Health and Safety at Work Act 1974 (HASAWA)* – this Act covers all employees and requires all employers to provide and maintain a safe system of working, safe place of work and competent work colleagues. The Act also requires employees to take care of their own health and safety and to cooperate with their employer in carrying out policies and procedures. Under the Act, many Regulations have been published which provide the detailed requirements; they are also known as *Statutory Instruments (SI)*. Regulations are the means by which EU Directives are implemented.

   The Health and Safety at Work Act 1974 (HASAWA) specifies a range of duties which employers have to comply with:
   - responsibility for safety in an organisation;
   - equipment;
   - materials – handling, storage and transport;
   - premises;
   - training and information.

The management of health and safety

The Management of Health and Safety at Work Regulations 1992 spell out requirements in more detail, for example the need to carry out risk assessments. The message in these Regulations is the importance of introducing an organised approach to health and safety based on planning, controlling, monitoring and reviewing. There are two crucial stages:

1 Preparation

You cannot establish a thorough health and safety system without proper preparation. You need to set up a document system which includes, for example:

- the organisation's health and safety policy;

- *health and safety procedures file* – these may have to be written specifically by or for the organisation, and may incorporate any guidance from professional bodies (for example the UKCC);
- *health and safety induction training file* – this could be included as a part of the overall induction for new staff; don't forget that existing staff will need to be inducted into the use of new equipment or new systems;
- *health and safety information file* – obtain current information about:
  - HASAWA and Regulations
  - manufacturers' information about equipment and substances;
- fire certificates, records of inspections: service and maintenance records;
- publications and guides which interpret the Act and Regulations in everyday language; copies of articles from journals.

2 *Assessment*

Employers need to assess the hazards and risks to their employees and take positive action to reduce these. Waiting for a problem to happen before action is taken is totally unacceptable.

Hazards and risks can be defined as follows:

> *Hazard* – 'anything which can cause harm, whether it is an activity like lifting, a substance like bleach, a machine, a wet floor, electricity etc.'
>
> National Care Homes Association 1993

Other common hazards are actions involving lifting and handling, steps, trailing leads (from vacuum cleaners etc.), storage of wheelchairs, damaged paths, windows which won't open easily, lift doors, water temperature.

> *Risk* – 'the likelihood that harm would be caused from a particular hazard. Lifting and wet floors would be examples of high risks in caring situations, whereas using a properly maintained machine like a washer/drier would be low risk'.
>
> National Care Homes Association 1993.

Risk assessment is broad-based and must include: equipment, premises, security of staff and clients, protection against violence, harassment, theft, passive smoking and stress.

Employers need to:

1 identify hazards;
2 assess the risk of each hazard;
3 record the findings;
4 take action to minimise these risks;
5 establish a monitoring system.

Some groups of employees present special risks and you must incorporate these extra needs as well, for example pregnant women, disabled people, older workers.

An example of an initial risk assessment checklist is given overleaf. This form was designed by the National Care Homes Association (1993).

HEALTH AND SAFETY ASSESSMENT

Initial check list

Name .... Date ....

Description	Location	Observations
Documentation: Policies Procedures		
Training arrangements: In house External		
First aid provision: Certificated Non certificated		
COSHH arrangements: Chemicals Body fluids Clinical wastes Drugs Water temperature		
Manual handling: Associated equipment		
Access: Floors Corridors Doorways Stairways Lifts		
Lighting: Artificial Natural		
Ventilation: Type Effectiveness		
Windows: Height Glass		
Electrical safety: Fixed Portable		
Protective equipment: Type Condition		
Kitchen safety: Physical Microbiological		

▶

Initial check list (continued)

Description	Location	Observations
Laundry safety: Physical Microbiological		
Outside areas: Structure Paths		
Vehicles: Control		
Violence to staff: Procedures		
Staff welfare provision: Rest room		

ACTIVITY

Under each of the following headings, give examples of ways in which your organisation complies with Health and Safety at Work Act 1974:

- equipment;
- materials;
- premises;
- training and information.

Employers also need to identify and record the names of the people who will be responsible for given areas of health and safety. Although they don't need to be technical experts – this may have to be bought in as and when required – they must be interested in and committed to health and safety: the task should never be regarded as simply a bureaucratic necessity. The person responsible needs the wisdom of Solomon and the nose of a bloodhound!

ACTIVITY

1 Talk to your staff about hazards and risks, and the need to assess. Ask them to spot as many hazards and risks as they can. You could divide responsibilities between team members – area by area or by type of hazard (for example electrical equipment or hazardous substances).
2 Ask staff to record their findings directly onto a copy of the assessment form. When this has been completed, discuss each hazard and assess the risk presented by each using a simple rating – for example high, medium and low risk. Deal with any high risks immediately.

ACTIVITY

Think back to the last health and safety problem in your place of work.

- How was it dealt with?
- Who handled the problem?
- What did you learn from this experience?
- What actions have been taken to prevent a recurrence of the problem?

ACTIVITY

Obtain the health and safety policy for your organisation. Consider the following questions:

- Does the policy cover all relevant aspects of health and safety? Does it provide practical guidance?
- Is the policy implemented in your unit or department?
- How could you do more to support this policy?

Several Regulations have very particular relevance to the care sector and these are outlined here.

Manual Handling Operations Regulations 1992

Accidents associated with manual handling are common in the care sector. For example, in the health services they form 50% of all reported accidents (with patient handling representing 70% of these). Back problems cause chronic pain and reduced mobility for far too many care workers.

The priorities in manual handling risks are to:

- *Avoid* manual handling operations where reasonably practicable – 'Does she/he/it need to be moved at all?'
- *Assess* in a suitable and sufficient manner any manual handling which cannot be avoided;
- *Reduce the risk* of injury so far as is reasonably practicable by introducing mechanical assistance; where this is not reasonably practicable then explore improvements to the task, the load and the working environment.

Specialist assessment may be required where manual handling operations are complex and varied. Someone with an outside perspective may not only reveal more hazards but may also suggest new solutions.

Mechanisation of handling tasks must be supported by proper maintenance and adequate staff training. In some situations such as residential homes for older people, clients and relatives will also need to be involved in the introduction of such equipment. Hoists and similar large pieces of machinery are generally obtrusive and certainly not conducive to a homely environment. Some clients may initially refuse to use the equipment. You need to be firm about this issue. If a formal assessment has revealed the need for a mechanical aid, then it must be used or the procedure not carried out at all. Staff should realise that refusal to use a mechanical aid after appropriate training could lead to disciplinary action. Without such a stand, employers cannot meet their legal responsibilities.

In care work, not all manual handling can be avoided even after full assessment, avoidance and mechanisation. This being the case, employers must establish satisfactory procedures for their staff. Note that the Regulations do not set out weight limits – as mentioned earlier the level of risk is determined by the interaction between the task, the load and the working environment.

Training should be relevant and on-going – people forget and can slip back into old and unsafe practices. Some employers invest in intensive training for one or two members of staff who then carry out in-house training for their colleagues. This approach can be better than sending all staff on a short course which deals only with general principles: training must be applied to the real work situation.

Control of Substances Hazardous to Health Regulations 1988

These Regulations are usually referred to as COSHH (pronounced 'cosh'!). Employers must assess the risks before any substances are introduced into the workplace. Assessment should be carried out by a competent person. For many care organisations – given the range of chemicals in use – this should be undertaken by someone with specialist knowledge.

Chemicals are classified and labelled as:

- very toxic;
- toxic;
- harmful;
- irritant;
- corrosive.

The Regulations cover harmful microorganisms (such as those contained in clinical waste) and dust in significant quantities, in addition to chemicals.

The main routes for exposure to these substances are:

- contact with skin;
- absorption through skin;
- inhalation;
- ingestion.

Problem areas for care organisations include:

- cleaning materials – for example bleach, disinfectants, metal cleaners, antiseptics;
- blood and other bodily fluids, discarded soiled dressings;
- gardening chemicals – for example weed killers and insecticides;
- decorating materials, for example white spirit;
- drugs – also covered by COSHH, although the control of drugs is determined by other legislation and the requirements of various statutory bodies (for example registration authorities).

Control measures include:

- checking that the substances are still needed;
- accurate labelling;
- safe storage, properly marked;
- protective clothing;
- safe procedures;
- first aid instructions – written down and kept close to the substance;
- information for staff;
- staff training.

Electricity at Work Regulations 1989

Electricity is so commonly used that its dangers can be forgotten. Because most people can change a plug, there is the further danger that many people think they are experts. All electrical systems must be constructed, used and maintained so as to sustain safety at all times. They can be divided into:

- *fixed electrical installation* – wiring, points, etc.
- *portable electrical appliances* – TVs, hair dryers, vacuum cleaners, lawn mower, etc.

The following actions are needed to stay within the Regulations:

- The installation should be professionally undertaken (by an IEE qualified contractor); tests should be carried out at least every five years and certificates kept safely. Maintenance must be carried out properly and records kept.
- You should keep a record of every portable appliance, either owned or hired by the organisation or used on its premises. Appliances must be inspected and tested by a competent person and the results recorded. Mark each appliance with an identity number and use this on your records. The frequency of inspection and testing will depend upon its usage; for example every month might be appropriate for a vacuum cleaner, every six months for an infrequently used electric keyboard. Plan the inspection and testing schedule in advance and stick to it. However, do remind staff that watching for hazards is a daily responsibility; a schedule does not lessen this need. 'The competent person' need not be a qualified electrician. However, be sensible about this and call in a

qualified electrician whenever you are in any doubt about a particular piece of equipment, a microwave oven for instance. Some larger organisations employ their own electricians who carry out the testing and inspection.

Checks should be carried out systematically. Points to look for include:

- discoloration of pins or plug body;
- discoloration of parts of appliances;
- loose plug tops;
- incorrect wiring of plug;
- incorrect fuse rating;
- cord grips not tightened down correctly;
- damaged flexible cord;
- unsafe joints in cord;
- damaged or faulty casing;
- faulty neon indicators;
- appliance has temporary or 'uncertified' repairs.
- appliance gives cause for concern for other reasons such as: inappropriate noise, smell, insufficient length of cord, etc.

> **ACTIVITY**
>
> In many care environments, clients are encouraged to own and use their own radios, TVs, electric shavers and so on. How can you ensure electrical safety without imposing unnecessary restrictions on clients? You might consider the following issues:
>
> - How will you inform clients of their responsibilities?
> - How will you ensure that clients use their equipment safely?

Workplace (Health, Safety and Welfare) Regulations 1992

These Regulations are being implemented in stages, between January 1993 and January 1996, and you should obtain current information to ensure that you are complying. The Regulations are concerned with the complete working environment and include:

- space;
- ventilation;
- lighting;
- temperature;
- provision of toilets and washing facilities;
- drinking water;
- changing rooms and rest facilities;
- fire precautions.

Health and Safety Display Screen Equipment Regulations 1992

These cover the use of computers and word processors. They apply only in organisations where staff can be classified as 'users' – in general someone who spends at least half their time on screen work. Most care workers will not be in this position but clerical staff might well be. In any case, it will be good practice to ensure that anyone using a computer can do so in reasonable comfort. Threats to health include repetitive strain injury (RSI) in the wrists and forearms, and radiation from monitors (screens).

Problems are aggravated by:

- poorly arranged work stations – inappropriate height of chairs, screens, keyboards or tables;
- too much time spent in screen work without adequate breaks.

Reporting of Injuries, Diseases and Dangerous Occurrences Regulations 1985

You have a responsibility to ensure that accidents are properly reported and recorded. These Regulations require employers to report certain types of events to the Health and Safety Executive or the local authority; they do not cover every eventuality which deserves proper documentation. Events covered by the Regulations are:

- fatal accidents;
- major injury accidents/conditions;
- dangerous occurrences;
- accidents causing more than three days incapacity for work;
- certain work-related diseases;
- certain matters dealing with the safe supply of gas.

Aside from the requirements of these Regulations, you must ensure that all accidents or 'untoward occurrences' are properly reported and recorded; an 'accident book' must be kept for this purpose. Claims for negligence can be brought up to three years after the event so it is important to record sufficient detail and to hold these records for the full three years. These details should include:

- date and time of the accident/occurrence;
- full name and occupation of the person affected;
- nature of the injury;
- details of any treatment given;
- place where the accident/occurrence happened – use diagrams/photos;
- full description of the incident – sequence of events, including the part played by other staff or clients.

7.4 Promoting health in the workplace

ACTIVITY

Consider the following questions:

- Does your organisation have a health promotion policy? If not, why do you think this is?
- Do you think that such a policy would be helpful?
- How could you initiate discussion about the development of a policy?
- Who would be the key 'interested parties' in your organisation? What would be the benefits to them of such a policy?

Over and above the obligations of the health and safety at work legislation, you should also consider how you can promote good health at work. The World Health Organisation defines health promotion as follows:

> 'Health promotion is the process of enabling people to increase control over, and to improve, their health.'
>
> WHO 1984

In a general sense, everything you do in your work may potentially have an impact on the health of staff, clients and yourself: the way you plan work, how you select staff, your leadership style and so on. All these activities contribute to the working climate, levels of stress and staff morale. As the WHO definition makes clear, health improvements depend on a personal sense of control. Encouraging staff involvement and autonomy will help individuals to feel more in control of their lives.

Many organisations have health promotion policies. These should be developed through wide ranging discussions with interested parties, such as supervisors, managers, staff, occupational health departments, trade unions and professional organisations. The health promotion service provided by the local health authority or Trust can offer specialist advice.

A health promotion policy might lead to specific health education programmes – to control smoking and alcohol, for example.

Smoking

The health hazards of smoking are well established. There have been many moves to reduce the amount of smoking in the workplace and reduce the damaging impact on non-smokers of passive smoking. Many employers have a no-smoking policy, with smokers confined to designated areas.

While these moves are to be welcomed, they may give rise to ethical problems in some sectors of care. Clients who have smoked for many years must have their lifestyles respected. You should encourage the development of policies which are sensitive to the individual needs of clients. At the same time, try to make everyone – staff and clients – aware of the dangers involved.

> **ACTIVITY**
>
> You have been asked by your manager to draft a smoking policy for your place of work.
>
> - Who should you involve in the discussions?
> - What difficulties would you anticipate?

Alcohol

The abuse of alcohol causes many lost working days and much chronic ill health. In addition, the social and domestic consequences of alcoholism are devastating. More and more employers are recognising this and have introduced quite severe policies including banning the consumption of alcohol on the premises and also on coming to work under the influence of alcohol. Some firms have made it clear that the 'liquid lunch' is no longer acceptable and could result in disciplinary action. Care-sector organisations have often taken a lead in this change of attitude and practice.

However, accompanying this hardening of approach, many employers are offering support to employees who recognise their problems and who are prepared to accept help. Larger employers may have counsellors on the staff who can help affected employees come to terms with their problems.

As with smoking, banning alcohol in the workplace can create ethical dilemmas. The positive effects of alcohol are rarely promoted but there can be no doubt of its role in helping people to relax in social situations. Many clients can benefit from social drinking within safe limits. For example, there

> **ACTIVITY**
>
> Is there an alcohol policy in your workplace? How was this developed? Who was involved and how is it monitored and reviewed? Discuss the policy with your colleagues. Does the policy receive general support?

> **ACTIVITY**
>
> Many organisations try to control smoking and alcohol but there are many other potential health risks.
>
> - What other risks does your organisation recognise formally? For instance, AIDS, stress and drug abuse.
> - What methods of health promotion and education are used for these? How successful are they?
> - How would you improve your organisation's approach to health promotion?

8 Planning and controlling resources

This Chapter covers the planning and control of the use of resources. Your responsibilities are likely to include three main areas:

- money;
- premises;
- materials, equipment and energy.

8.1 Managing money

Every manager has financial responsibilities. You may be asked to provide information and ideas to contribute to the development of budgets. Whether or not you have to prepare a budget yourself, you will always have to monitor how money is spent.

Whatever your precise responsibilities, you need to understand what budgets are about and the ways in which you can best use your experience and expertise to meet the financial objectives of your organisation. It is essential that you are able to monitor and control costs effectively. Although you may find some of the material in this section new or difficult, it will begin to make sense when you apply it to your own setting.

Budgets

A budget is *a plan expressed in financial terms*. More specifically, it is an estimate of income and expenditure for a future period. A budget shows the cost of the activities expected to take place during the forthcoming period – usually the next financial year.

Cost centres

A cost centre is any part of the organisation with a budget attached to it. It could be a department, a ward, a service (such as a community service or chiropody service) or an individual practitioner or clinician (such as a surgeon). Usually, each cost centre has a budget holder, in other words the individual who is responsible for that particular budget. In a computerised finance system, a cost centre usually possesses both a name and a number (for example 'Highgrove Locality Team' might also be known as 'LT24').

Expense category or code

Each type of expenditure is also given an individual number – in other words it is coded, to show, for example, the amounts spent on cleaning, stationery or staffing. This is so that you can easily analyse the total costs of running cost centres.

Time period

All budgets are for specific periods. As a rule, a twelve month period is the basis for financial planning, for instance the period 1 April to 31 March of the following year.

Budget reports

You should receive regular budget reports or statements showing income and expenditure. Once a month is usual. If less often, you may become aware of problems too late to correct easily.

Types of budgeting

There are several approaches to developing a budget, each of which has its advantages and disadvantages.

Incremental budgeting

Using this method, you take the current year's spending (actual or forecast) as the basis for the following year's budget plans. You then make adjustments to allow for price rises, salary increases and so on. This is also known as *historical budgeting* and it makes the assumption that activity in the following year will be virtually unchanged from the current year. In stable situations, this approach saves the time and expense involved in reviewing and costing every activity.

In health and care organisations, there are some core activities which will be similar from year to year. For example, a nursery will continue to care for its complement of children; or a hospital ward will still need to provide care for a particular type of patient. Although there will be some changes in both of these situations – more or fewer clients, for instance – the current year's figures can form a realistic basis for the following year's budget calculations.

A danger of the incremental approach is that you could become complacent, failing to see when parts of the service have become irrelevant, or where improvements in efficiency can be made.

A further disadvantage of incremental budgeting is that it cannot easily take into account long term or complex projects to which the organisation is committed. For example, a health service Trust may wish to develop a community care initiative for people with learning difficulties involving several cost centres, including wards and occupational therapy departments.

Programme budgeting

Incremental budgeting generally uses existing cost centres as sources of information about future costs and income. Cross-departmental programmes can be difficult to get off the ground. However, by taking the project, or *programme*, as the most important unit in budgeting, different cost centres are linked more closely to the goals and objectives of the organisation.

An important advantage of this process is that the benefits, as well as the costs, of the programme are taken into account. 'Cost-benefit analysis' is

> **ACTIVITY**
>
> Alice Helms supervises a social services day unit for adults with mental health problems. She wants to increase her spending on publicity, which has been very low, to try to reach more clients in the rural areas. She is faced with making the case to her manager for more money. She needs to show that there is a reasonable chance that the benefits gained will be worth the money spent.
>
> What points do you think Alice should make to her manager? What extra information would Alice need to develop her proposal? You should consider the following issues:
>
> - How might Alice measure the benefits of this change?
> - What types of publicity might be appropriate?
> - What might be the resource implications of more clients?

crucial in ensuring that money is not wasted on projects which may appear to be valuable but which bring little or no actual benefit to clients.

To summarise, the advantages of programme budgeting are that it:

- recognises the organisation's goals and objectives;
- cuts across departmental boundaries;
- deals with long term plans;
- examines the relationship between costs and benefits.

Zero-based budgeting

As its name implies, zero-based budgeting involves planning and costing individual activities from scratch. In principle, zero-based budgeting should produce the most accurate forecasts of activity, income and expenditure. The problem is that it can be extremely expensive to carry out.

In practice, many care organisations use several types of budgeting. Often, an incremental approach is used to estimate the bulk of income and expenditure. Zero-based budgeting is then used to focus attention on a specific part of the overall budget. For example, although the core activity of a residential home is to provide residential care, there may also be an interest in diversifying into day and domiciliary care. In this case, an incremental approach is adopted for the residential component and a zero-based approach used for the day and domiciliary care provision because this is new and likely to change considerably, especially in the first year or two.

It is good practice to adopt a zero-based approach to a different proportion (say 25%) of the budget each year. A critical review of the methods, costs and benefits within a selected part of a budget should improve efficiency. In this way, it is possible to review the organisation's complete budget over a four year period.

Preparing a budget

The budget cycle

Try to see budgeting as a continuous cycle of activity. You need to know about how budgets are put together, what should be done and when – in other words the nature of the budget cycle. As we have seen, most budgets are intended to cover a twelve month period – the financial year. The following diagram shows how the different parts of the budget cycle fit together.

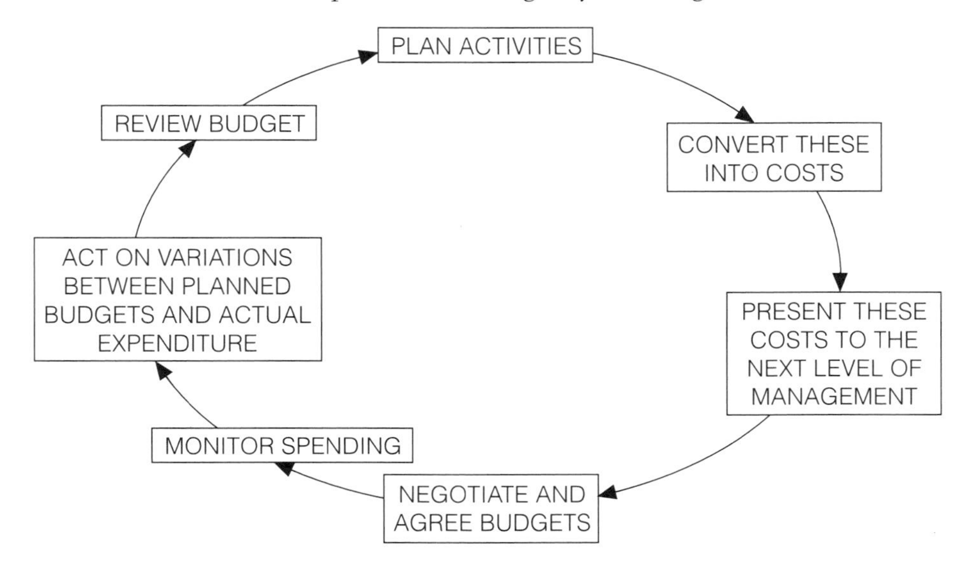

Budget components

Most budgets include the following components:

- *Staffing costs*, for example salaries and staff-related costs;
- *Consumables*, for example food and stationery;
- *Services*, for example laundry, cleaning, maintenance of equipment and telephone costs;
- *Fixed establishment costs*, for example rent, rates, and insurance;
- *Depreciation*, concerned with fixed assets.

Staffing costs can be broken down as follows:

- *Basic salary* – determined by the following, depending upon the organisation:
  - grade
  - incremental point
  - annual cost of living increase;

  Some employers appoint staff to a point on a salary scale with increments being automatically applied each year until the top of the scale is reached. Others make appointments at a single salary level; in these cases, employees may receive an annual 'cost of living' increase (usually linked to a national inflation index). In other cases, staff may have to earn an increase depending on an assessment of their performance during the past year; this is often known as performance-related pay (PRP);
- *Overtime* – if applicable;
- *Sessional (or part time) staff* – the costs of employing staff to carry out specific tasks for specific periods, perhaps on an hourly rate. For instance, staff who are contracted through agencies;
- *Staff-related costs* (often known as 'on-costs'):
  - national insurance: the employer's contribution
  - superannuation: the employer's contribution
  - performance-related pay (if applicable).

Depreciation deals with the use of 'fixed assets'. Fixed assets are items of equipment or premises which have a life longer than one year. These kinds of items of equipment lose value as time goes by through 'wear and tear'. As a result, an investment of £1000.00 in a piece of equipment in one year may only be worth, say, £800.00 the following year. You may be all too familiar with this factor when it comes to buying and selling cars. In accounting terms, this type of loss by depreciation is seen as a kind of expenditure. When replacing a car, the loss in value of your present car will influence whether you can buy a Lada or a Ferrari next time around!

Ideally, budgets should be prepared from the bottom up, in other words by the level of management closest to the point where income is earned or costs incurred. In the case of care sector organisations, this usually means 'closest to the client'. These budget estimates are submitted to your line manager who then produces an aggregate budget. An aggregate budget is the total of all the budgets submitted to the particular manager concerned. This same process continues up the organisation until a single, overall budget is produced.

Your budget must be realistic – the financial expression of a carefully thought out plan of activities. You should not prepare it in isolation. Ask for the views of your team when you are reviewing the past period and developing your plans for the forthcoming year. By doing this, you will get the widest range of ideas and encourage staff to feel involved. Budget proposals should take into account:

- activities which are desirable;
- activities which are realistic;
- the overall financial expectations of the organisation.

There is little point in recommending plans, however impressive, which demand more money than is likely to be available in the near future. This does not mean, however, that you should ignore longer term needs. Draw them to the attention of your manager but bear in mind that it might be counter-productive to cost them in detail at too early a stage.

Managing spending

Once you have been allocated a budget, your responsibilities do not stop – in fact, they are only just beginning. You will have to:

- *monitor* whether you are spending too much or too little;
- *analyse* overspends or underspends to find out the reasons for any variations appearing on your budget reports;
- *act* to deal with any variations.

To manage spending effectively, you need to understand the basics of the systems that accountants have developed to record, monitor and analyse expenditure.

A *ledger* is the system in which accountants record the financial transactions of an organisation. You will be particularly interested in the record of your spending. Many ledger systems are computerised; however, for small organisations, a manual system may be more than adequate.

Computerised ledger systems can produce a wide variety of reports to help you understand what is happening to your income and your spending. Although you should receive written budget reports at regular intervals, do develop good links with the member of staff in the finance department responsible for your particular cost centre. This will help you to understand some of the accounting jargon and procedures which are an inevitable part of organisational life. Equally importantly, you will be in a better position to influence the kind of information you receive and how it is presented.

In many cases, expenditure doesn't occur evenly across a twelve month period. For example, if you manage a residential home, you may plan to take residents on holiday during July in a minibus. Because of this, your spending on fuel, and possibly other expenses, will rise significantly during this period. Where you can predict peaks and troughs, you should indicate this in your initial budget proposals. If you don't, you may find yourself overspending in particular categories during July. In the longer run, these differences may well cancel themselves out but you should do what you can to avoid these problems. Planning budgetary peaks and troughs across the year is known as '*budget profiling*'. For the example just given, you might predict the following profile:

Fuel – budget for the year = £1500.00			
January	50.00	July	350.00
February	50.00	August	200.00
March	100.00	September	150.00
April	100.00	October	100.00
May	150.00	November	50.00
June	150.00	December	50.00

This budget profile estimates that there will be a greater usage during the warmer months of the year, especially in July when the residents go on holiday.

Inaccurate profiling can cause severe cash-flow problems and has been the cause of many business failures.

Making sense of budget reports

You need to become familiar with how budget reports are prepared and presented in your organisation. An example of a report is given below. Notice that this example relates to a particular time period – one month. Both the planned budget and the spending are based on this period.

DANELEIGH DAY CENTRE — Cost Centre No. 48
Budget Holder: JUDITH McCLEOD

Budget Report — Period: 03 (to end June)

	Current month budget (1)	*Current month expenditure (2)*	*Budget for year (3)*	*Budget to date (4)*	*Expenditure to date (5)*	*Variance to date (6)*
Travel	42	39	500	126	157	31
Materials	292	307	3500	876	905	29
Utilities	100	92	1200	300	234	–66
Food	250	298	3000	750	784	34
Stationery	42	39	500	126	109	–17

(1) the amount planned to be spent during this month (see 'budget profiling' on page 91).
(2) the amount actually spent during this month.
(3) the amount planned to be spent by the end of the financial year.
(4) the amount planned to be spent by this stage of the year.
(5) the amount actually spent during the year so far.
(6) the difference between the expenditure to date (5) and the budget to date (4) (see 'variances' on page 93).

The meaning of a budget report depends on the kind of accounting system used in your organisation. As a budget holder, you need to know when an expense is actually entered on to the ledger. This is significant because the period between ordering an item and paying for it can be a long one. There are three alternatives:

1 Commitment accounting

In commitment accounting, the cost of a piece of equipment or a service is entered on to the ledger at the time that the order is placed, in other words when the commitment to spend is made. Entry does not wait until the equipment has arrived or the service is carried out. This system has an advantage in that you have a clearer idea of both what you have actually spent *and* the amount you have committed to spend. As long as you keep a close eye on your budget reports, you should be able to avoid overspending with this form of accounting.

If commitment accounting is in use, you only have to take note of when the commitment has been made; delivery dates and payment dates are irrelevant. It takes no account of cash flow or matching income with expenditure which is why it has serious limitations. Not all commitments can be fulfilled, for example goods may be unavailable for long periods or a contractor may not be able to carry out a service.

2 Accrual accounting

Accrual accounting is the most common kind of accounting system. It differs from commitment accounting in that expenditure is only entered on the ledger when payment becomes unavoidable, for example when a piece of equipment has been delivered, or when a service has been carried out.

Computerised accounting systems can often give you both accrual and commitment information. You should find this very helpful because it will display both expenditure actually incurred and that which is due to be incurred.

3 Cash-flow accounting

In this system, only the cash actually paid out is recorded in the budget reports. Future commitments are ignored. The obvious disadvantage is that you cannot simply disregard future commitments – you will have to record them separately and bear them in mind when you receive your budget reports.

To summarise, the difference between commitment, accrual and cash-flow accounting is based on when the expenditure or income is entered into the ledger. If you know this, you will be able to interpret your budget reports more accurately and stay in control of your finances.

Sometimes you will find it difficult to balance income and expenditure in a single year. Every organisation has financial rules intended to control the amount of money that a cost centre is allowed to 'carry over' into the next financial year; this amount may be expressed as a percentage of the budget. Be aware that a carry-over figure, if allowed at all, can be either positive or negative – you could have to start the year in debt!

Monitoring and managing spending

Once you have a clear idea of your budget, and how the budget reports will be prepared, your main task is the day-to-day monitoring and management of spending. Look for differences between what you have spent, on the one hand, and the allocated budget, on the other. Differences of this kind are known as variances.

The variance can mean different things to different people but the following formula is one common way of expressing it:

VARIANCE = EXPENDITURE – BUDGET

Using this formula, if you spend £50.00 on stationery in any one budget period, when the allocated budget is £45.00 for the same period, the variance is £5.00, in other words you have overspent by £5.00.

On the other hand, if the allocated budget is £60.00, the variance is –£15.00 (£45.00 – £60.00), this means you have underspent by £15.00. A negative variance is sometimes indicated by a bracket, for example (£15.00), rather than by a minus sign. Where a variance is positive, as in the £5.00 example given above, it is conventional to leave out the plus sign, thus £5.00 is the same as +£5.00. There is more than one way of presenting variances in reports and you need to ensure that you are clear about the conventions used by the accountant in your organisation.

It is rarely possible to spend at exactly the rate predicted, with the exception of fixed expenditures, for example, rents or subscriptions to newspapers and magazines where you know exactly how much you will be charged and when. With experience, you will be able to judge when a variance has become significant and requires corrective action. You may be given guidance on this from a senior manager who may ask you to comment on variances which are greater than a predetermined percentage.

Regular budget reports provide you with a powerful means of detecting trends in over or underspending which will enable you to act when necessary. As you become more familiar with the different components of the budget, you will be able to attend to those variances which are unexpectedly high. Some of the common reasons for variances are:

- *Staff costs* – such as:
  - grading differences between new and previous staff;
  - pay awards which have not been reflected in the budget;
  - increases in overtime, due to maternity leave, sick leave, unplanned study leave, and so on;
  - changes in skill mix occurring in mid-year. In some public sector organisations, such as NHS Trusts, skill mix review has been widely undertaken and has had a significant impact on the staffing budget.
- *Non-staff costs* – such as:
  - changes in practice resulting in the need for different materials and equipment;
  - a higher overall level of activity and demand for the services you offer, for example more clients, or the same number of more dependent clients;
  - a change in the pattern of ordering, leading to unanticipated peaks and troughs.
- *Mistakes* – Don't ignore human error as a possible source of variance. Ledger entries can be incorrect for a whole host of reasons – misunderstandings, 'slips of the pen', or miscodings, for instance.

Income generation

Increasingly, care sector organisations are having to consider ways in which they can raise income. In the past, most public sector organisations were concerned mainly with controlling spending. Income was important, of course, but individual managers had little control over it.

Changes in government policy have encouraged managers in all sectors to pay more attention to how they can generate income, as well as to how they can control their expenditure. Private sector disciplines and priorities have become part and parcel of public sector life.

The scope for income generation will vary considerably with the type of organisation. Examples are as follows:

- a hospital rents out space in its foyer for commercial use by florists and newsagents;

ACTIVITY

The presence or absence of plus or minus signs in budget reports often causes concern and confusion in otherwise well-balanced individuals! Don't be put off – few of us are budding accountants. If you find yourself getting 'number block', pause for a while and go back to basics. Remind yourself of the first principles outlined in this section and remember the variance formula.

Look for examples of positive and negative variances in the sample report on page 92. Do the calculations yourself to make sure you can see how the figures have been produced. Always go back to your local financial experts – management accountant, finance officer and so on – and ask them to make things clear for you.

- a residential home hires out accommodation for use by the University of the Third Age;
- a day centre obtains sponsorship from a local organisation to subsidise day trips for clients;
- an NHS Trust organises and charges for short courses for people who want to lose weight.

Managing a budget can be daunting. Do your best to keep ahead. The following are a few tips to help you survive.

1. *Know what your budgetary responsibilities are.* This may sound obvious but it is surprising how many managers accept rather than agree their budgets.
2. *Understand the financial reports on your spending.* Most reports are produced by accountants, not care managers. Because of this, the presentation may be very unfamiliar. Make every effort you can to identify the really important figures. Not all are equally significant and you need to discuss this with the accountant so that you can monitor your spending accurately and economically. Many very senior managers have experienced serious difficulties understanding their budget reports, so you should never feel inhibited about saying you don't understand. Always ask, and go on asking until things make sense to you!
3. *Find out what is being charged to your budget.* Discover exactly what the various codes mean. Keep an eye out for costs that might have been charged to your cost centre by error or misunderstanding.
4. *Make time to analyse your financial reports.* Don't put this off. If a trend in over- or underspending is developing, you should try to detect this earlier rather than later. A problem which has been allowed to grow may require drastic action later!

8.2 Managing premises

You are responsible for ensuring that the premises under your control are used effectively, efficiently and safely. Depending on your particular circumstances, these responsibilities include:

- general maintenance;
- the state of the decoration;
- how well areas are signposted;
- the efficient use of rooms;
- the state of the gardens.

Large organisations will employ specialists to deal with such things – the Estates Manager, for example. In small community homes, by contrast, managers may be expected to operate very much like normal householders, such as arranging for repairs to be carried out, rooms to be decorated and so on. In some cases, it will make sense for you to delegate the day-to-day management of some of these responsibilities, for example fixtures and fittings, the garden and so on.

Where many responsibilities are devolved to small units, you need to consider the implications for you, for example any increased responsibilities, such as arranging adequate insurance and ensuring that the premises meet health and safety requirements.

You should to be prepared to deal with unexpected requests. For example, voluntary groups might ask if they can use your premises. You might be able to arrange this at a nominal cost, or no cost at all. In other cases, you might have to charge a market price. Work within the guidelines set out by your own employer. Sometimes there are ethical, as well as economic, implications to be taken into account, as suggested by the following activity.

Always involve those clients who normally use the premises – residents, day centre users for instance – in any discussions as to whether to extend the use of the premises.

ACTIVITY

You are a charge nurse responsible for a group home for people with learning difficulties who also have sensory problems – some residents are deaf, others have very restricted vision. You have been asked by a representative of a local voluntary group for older people if they can use your premises one evening a week to hold classes for the University of the Third Age.

How would you respond to this request? Try to identify the possible factors that you should consider. Here are some suggestions:

- the wishes of the residents;
- access to the premises;
- possible advantages for the residents themselves;
- financial considerations, for example costs to the home, charges, reciprocal arrangements.

8.3 Managing materials and equipment

All organisations need a regular supply of materials and equipment in order to carry out their functions. The range of resources is very wide, for example:

- machinery;
- stationery;
- laundry;
- food;
- drugs and chemicals;
- care equipment – such as dressings and splints;

- electricity and gas;
- petrol and diesel fuels.

As a budget holder, you will have to control the spending on some of these. This may be through direct purchases, as in buying food, or through controlling activities, such as staff travel.

Prices of very similar items can vary considerably and you will have to advise your manager when you feel that the organisation's money could be better spent. In general, you should try to:

- give your staff as much information as you can about the cost of the materials and energy sources they use; encourage everyone to think before they act;
- use your budget reports, so that you can see how spending is going; give quick feedback to your team if the reports suggest that a problem is looming;
- review who is able to authorise particular requisitions; custom and practice may need to be reconsidered if you feel that the controls on spending are too loose;
- listen to your team and encourage their involvement in cost controls; a good argument for using an expensive item of equipment can still win the day if it can be shown to represent good value for money.

Acquiring materials and equipment

To make an effective case for more resources, you must be able to show that you have estimated the relevant costs and benefits.

Costs

There are three types of cost you need to estimate:

- acquisition costs (assessing the product, delivery charges, additional costs such as the need to make extra space);
- running costs (repairs and maintenance, energy);
- opportunity costs (what else could the money be used for?).

Benefits

These can be difficult to quantify, especially in the health and social care sector. Nevertheless, a good case must try to identify as many concrete benefits as possible, without forgetting those that are less easily measured. Examples include:

- *greater productivity* – for example, a new computer might save staff time in completing records; fitting a ramp would enable a day centre to offer its service to wheelchair users;
- *increased efficiency* – for instance, a computerised accounting system could save a care home money in professional book-keeping fees;
- *improved quality of service* – for example, new furniture which is more comfortable for clients; benefits like this are sometimes difficult to justify in strictly financial terms but can improve the quality of client care.

ACTIVITY

Think of the last item of equipment you were responsible for purchasing. Consider the following questions:

- How well did the process go?
- How did you go about making your case?
- Whom did you consult? Was this consultation process effective?
- Were you able to identify clear costs and benefits?

Receiving materials and equipment

Every organisation needs an effective procedure for receiving new materials – including thorough inspection, proper installation and informing appropriate staff of the arrival so that invoices can be paid.

Most procedures involve several steps:

1. *Advice notes* – sent by a manufacturer letting you know that goods are in transit; they include details of the goods being delivered (for example all or part of the order), delivery method, anticipated date of delivery and your order number.
2. *Delivery notes* – sent with the goods; they contain a description of the goods, including costs, and your order number.
3. *Invoice* – a document sent by the supplier listing the goods or services supplied and stating the amount of money due.

Delivery notes should be passed to the department responsible for paying the invoice. Without evidence of delivery, payment cannot be authorised.

Storing materials

How you decide to store materials will depend on how well you have analysed your particular needs. You should think about:

- available space;
- storage – you need to satisfy health and safety requirements;
- security – some materials, such as syringes and needles, are a common target for theft and must be locked away securely;
- how you will monitor the use of these materials.

ACTIVITY

List the materials you are personally responsible for.
What are the major concerns you have about each of these?
Do you have a computerised system of stock control available to you?
How could you improve the storage of each of these materials?

Managing stock

How do you decide how much to stock? You should take into account two factors:

1. the need to have materials available when staff need them;
2. the need to avoid stocking more than is necessary.

To balance these two demands, you need to further analyse your own situation. Separate the importance of different types of materials by considering the following questions. Which materials:

- must you have available at all times?
- could you do without for a short time?

ACTIVITY

Take a thorough look at your area of responsibility. How much of the current stock is

- essential?
- of doubtful value, at least in present quantities?
- definitely not needed in the foreseeable future?

This activity is not designed to highlight your inadequacies. Over time, all of us tend to acquire more than we need, for many good reasons. The point is that, on a regular and planned basis, you should take an objective look at how you are doing and then try to correct things if need be.

Controlling costs

You should ensure that:

- materials bought are appropriate to the task;
- materials used are appropriate to the task;
- stocks are minimised;
- stock is used in sequence – notice how supermarkets always try to bring the oldest products to the front of the shelves to encourage customers to buy them first;
- stocks are stored in ideal conditions to minimise waste;
- staff are informed of any changes – for example when a switch of brand is made;
- staff are aware of the cost of the materials they consume.

ACTIVITY

Think about the materials you buy on a regular basis. Are you sure that they are the most appropriate to the task?
You can sometimes be surprised by your findings.

For example, the manager of a care home for people with physical disabilities decided to buy a 'better quality' toilet paper, namely one with more sheets per roll. However, the rolls were thicker and, because residents lacked some degree of manual dexterity, they tended to drop and accidentally dirty them, resulting in unnecessary waste. The manager reverted to the original, smaller rolls. Because she had to change them more frequently, she could maintain better hygiene. The point is that every problem is unique and needs its own solution.

8.4 Energy and environmental issues

Concern for the environment has grown enormously in recent years. Individuals, pressure groups and governments have each expressed their worries and suggested agendas for action. For many organisations wishing to take some action to help the 'green' lobby, the problem is knowing what to do at an everyday level: this can seem overwhelming, leading to paralysis in decision-making.

Without going into a detailed analysis and evaluation of the fundamental issues – well beyond the scope of this book – here are 10 questions to ask about your own organisation. What matters most is that these issues should be openly and widely discussed, and that everyone feels committed to securing the future of our environment.

1. *Does your organisation have a clearly stated environmental policy?* All organisations need to think about this and ensure that their ideas are publicised to employees and clients.
2. *Does your organisation buy 'environmentally-friendly' products?* Examples are recycled paper (stationery and toilet rolls), biodegradable cleaning materials and soaps which have not been animal-tested.
3. *Does your organisation conserve water?* This can be achieved by, for example, recycling waste water, collecting rain water for watering indoor plants and installing taps which cannot be left running accidentally.

4 *Does your organisation save electricity and gas?* Some ways in which this can be done are by:
   - using low power light bulbs;
   - installing efficient heating systems (for example computer-controlled);
   - considering alternative energy sources;
   - labelling appliances indicating the cost of energy used;
   - giving incentives to staff or departments which show they can save energy;
   - publicising the value of energy conservation.
5 *Does your organisation provide organic food?* Sometimes arrangements with local suppliers can keep the costs down.
6 *Does your organisation recycle waste where appropriate?* Local authorities are now providing collection points for a wider range of waste products, for example paper, glass and textiles.
7 *Does your organisation encourage staff to share cars, or to use alternative means of transport?* Staff will be encouraged to change their behaviour if employers take a responsible approach, for example by providing adequate bicycle facilities and staff showers.
8 *Does your organisation involve clients in environmental issues?* The views of clients and their relatives, as appropriate, are crucial. You should not assume anything about what clients' views might be. Ask and discuss. Make it part of the way you work. Concern for the environment can be seen as a very positive way of bringing people together to achieve common goals.
9 *Does your organisation demonstrate an understanding of the problems in the developing world?* The need for equal opportunities should not stop at national borders. Some organisations have created links with similar institutions in developing countries. This can help to bring about higher levels of mutual understanding and respect.
10 *Does your organisation include environmental issues as topics within its training programmes?*

Reading on ...

★ Jones, Rowan and Pendlebury, Maurice (1992) *Public Sector Accounting*, Pitman Publishing Inc, London.

9 People to do the job

People are the most important resource for any care organisation. This chapter deals with how to recruit and select staff who are well motivated and competent to do the job.

The time, effort and money spent in getting the best people are investments for the future. While money should never be wasted, for example by inappropriate advertising, false economies at this stage could be regretted later.

The part you play in recruitment and selection will differ according to the organisation you work for. Large organisations usually have personnel departments responsible for recruiting staff; they work closely with managers to make sure that the recruitment and selection procedures are effective. In smaller organisations, recruitment may be carried out by managers personally, sometimes with little or no administrative or clerical support.

RECRUITMENT

1. Decide whether job is needed.
2. Write the job description.
3. Write the person specification.
4. Assess the market – decide how to advertise.
5. Prepare an information pack for prospective applicants.

SELECTION

6. Devise a selection procedure.
7. Shortlist applicants.
8. Interview applicants.
9. Offer the post.
10. Deal with the aftermath, for example unsuccessful applicants.

9.1 Recruitment

Organisations need to recruit because staff have left (resigned, retired or been dismissed) or because a new post has been created.

Before going ahead with recruitment, always ask whether:

- *an existing job is still needed* – for example, has this particular job become irrelevant because clients' needs have changed?
- *there are better ways of achieving the same aims* – for example, could a full-time post be divided into two part-time posts, or vice versa?
- *a new post is justified.*

Skill mix

Most of an organisation's budget goes on staff costs so getting the staffing right is critical to economic survival. Most important is how to get the right levels of skill in the right places at the right times. For example, it is wasteful to employ a professionally qualified person to do a job that could be carried out by someone less qualified. Similarly, if specific skills are needed primarily in the daytime there is no point in having them concentrated in the night staff, and vice versa. These problems are solved by deciding on the most appropriate 'skill mix' and then recruiting and deploying staff to achieve it.

Patterns of employment

The health and social care sectors use many different employment patterns. The range of options includes:

- Full-time, permanent posts;
- Part-time, permanent posts;
- Full- and part-time posts, on temporary or fixed-term contracts (for example six months or two years);
- Job share – two or more people fill a single post and are responsible for organising the necessary cover between them;
- Agency staff – commercial agencies can provide a source of staff; some specialise in a particular group, for example nurses or social workers; others deal with a wide range of skills;
- 'Bank' staff – a 'bank' of staff is similar to an agency but is run by the organisation itself; it has been used widely in nursing where many clinical units build up a team of staff who work on a casual basis; sometimes full-time staff also offer their services to the bank, outside their normal hours of employment.

This increasing flexibility has led to many staff having more than one job. This in turn has implications for the commitment of staff to any particular place of work, staff training and their familiarity with local policies and procedures.

ACTIVITY

Here are two instances where an organisation might want to change its personnel requirements and therefore need to recruit different staff.

A Mrs Jenkins, the owner of a large nursing home, has been discussing with local general practitioners the possibility of offering a home care service to their patients. As a result, she thinks it viable to create the new post of 'Project Manager – Home Care' on a one year contract. She does not want to commit herself for longer than one year in case funding from the GPs does not materialise or the demand from patients is not there.

B Aminah Sutton manages a nursery in an inner city area. Children from many different cultural backgrounds attend each day and Aminah has been trying for some time to increase the activities available to the children. A member of the full-time staff has just retired and this has given Aminah the chance to rethink what is needed. She decides to advertise for two half-time staff rather than replace with another full-time person. By doing this, she hopes to recruit people who are able to offer two different sets of skills and experiences.

Having read through both of these cases, consider the following questions:

- What are the strengths and weaknesses of the actions proposed?
- What other alternatives might have been used?
- In your own place of work, are there:
  - jobs which are no longer needed? Why?
  - new jobs which need to be created? Why?
  - different ways of meeting the demands of existing jobs?

ACTIVITY

Ruth is a Senior Staff Nurse working in a day care unit for older people. There have been a number of problems recently with transport arrangements for clients; some have been arriving very late and the communication between the unit and the various transport agencies has been difficult to say the least. The unit manager is proposing to employ another Senior Staff Nurse and to divide the responsibilities between Ruth and the new member of staff, perhaps by giving one person the main clinical responsibility while the other takes on the administrative burden. The unit manager asks for Ruth's views.

Ruth decides to put forward an alternative. She suggests that, instead of employing another staff nurse, the manager ought to consider increasing the number of administrative staff in the unit. In Ruth's opinion, this would:

- deal more directly with what appears to be mainly an administrative problem;
- avoid any confusion of roles that might occur between two senior staff nurses;
- be cheaper.

When asked for more detail, Ruth goes on to suggest that an administrative assistant could be employed on a one year contract so that the effectiveness of the post could be reviewed before settling on a more permanent solution.

What do you think of Ruth's suggestions? What are the advantages and disadvantages?

Job descriptions

A job description is a document setting out the job to be done. By preparing a job description, you can decide whether a proposed job will fit in with the organisation's current and likely future needs. Most organisations try to keep job descriptions flexible. However, they need to be sufficiently detailed to give any interested person a reasonable idea of what the job is likely to expect of them.

Here are two examples of job descriptions. The headings have been taken from real job descriptions; the details are fictitious.

The first is a job description for an assistant manager in Eastly House, a social services home for people with learning difficulties.

Job Title:	*Assistant Manager*
Grade:	Scale 6
Reports to:	Manager
Job Purpose:	To be responsible to the manager for the day-to-day organisation, administration and development of a staff group. This will include financial and other resources delegated to the group. To utilise and develop departmental and community resources to the benefit of the service.
Dimensions:	Delegated responsibility from the manager for (a) 6–10 staff, (b) the clients within the home in the absence of the manager, and (c) control of expenditure totalling £25,000 per annum.
Job Context:	The Social Service Department has a duty to provide facilities for people with learning difficulties. For some people, this means living in a community home. Community homes mostly accommodate people who have been discharged from long-term institutional settings or who can no longer be accommodated within their family homes. The Assistant Manager is a member of the management team of the home and, as such, takes responsibility for the proper administration of the home and for the professional service that it provides.
Organisation:	Home Manager | Assistant Manager | Senior Care Worker | Care Workers

Main Activities:

1. To undertake day-to-day management in the absence of the Manager.
2. To share in care planning, case conferences and in promoting the development of good practice in the home.
3. To be aware of new practices and approaches in relevant areas of work.
4. To maintain close links with educational institutions, social and health workers in order to promote, develop and enhance a high standard of care through a multidisciplinary approach.
5. To develop links with community and voluntary organisations, with a view to the fuller integration of clients into the community.
6. Any other duties which may reasonably be required.

The second is a post for a care assistant in a small home for older people.

Job Title:	*Care Assistant*
Responsible to:	The Proprietor/Manager
Context and values:	When carrying out the responsibilities outlined in this job description, the care assistant should ensure that:

1 the client is respected at all times;
2 the client's independence is encouraged as far as possible;
3 language and other forms of communication used are suitable for the needs of the client;
4 the cultural, racial and religious identity if the client is respected;
5 the emotional needs of the client consistent with the role of care assistant are met as far as possible;
6 confidentiality of all information and sources is respected and disclosure is made only to those who necessarily require it;
7 all Health and Safety requirements and precautions are correctly applied.

Specific Responsibilities: A care assistant will be required to carry out the following:

1 assist residents with personal hygiene;
2 assist residents with grooming;
3 assist residents with mobility;
4 assist residents with group living;
5 assist residents to maintain a clean, healthy and safe living environment;
6 assist residents to eat and drink;
7 assist residents to manage continence;
8 contribute to the assessment of residents;
9 contribute to the administration of residents' medication;
10 prepare and cook food and drink as appropriate;
11 promote residents' living skills;
12 promote residents' social and communication skills;
13 assist residents with behaviour difficulties;
14 organise simple activities for individuals and groups;
15 contribute to the protection of residents and their rights;
16 maintain a healthy and safe environment;
17 respond to emergencies.

ACTIVITY

Look at the two job descriptions in this section.

- In what ways are they different?
- Why do you think there are differences and are they important?
- How helpful do you think the descriptions are to a prospective applicant? Is any other information needed?

Neither job description includes details of pay or conditions, or general information about the organisation or the geographical area. This kind of information is usually put into an information pack which accompanies the job description and application form.

Notice that the care assistant job description is much more specific about the tasks needed. Many of these were based on a set of standards identified by the Care Sector Consortium and so are related to the National or Scottish Vocational Qualifications (NVQ/SVQs) available in the care sector. Because NVQ/SVQs are derived from the standards needed in actual work, they can be used for many different purposes, including preparing job descriptions and organising in-house training. NVQ/SVQs are discussed in Chapter 10.

Person specification

As well as describing the job to be done, you also need to describe the kind of person needed to fill the post. This is known as a person specification. A clear specification helps enormously in shortlisting, interviewing and making a final decision. It is a reference point which can reduce bias and promote equal opportunities. The qualities needed are often divided into those that are essential and those that are desirable.

Using the earlier examples, possible person specifications are as follows:

Person Specification – Assistant Manager

	Essential	Desirable
Qualifications	CQSW, CSS, DipSW, C&G 325/2 or 325/3, RNMH	Relevant post-qualifying courses
Work Experience	At least two years in a relevant post in social or health care	1 Experience in a supervisory management role 2 Experience of multi-professional working
Skills, abilities, knowledge	1 An awareness of the implications of learning difficulty for the individual 2 Knowledge of current care philosophies and practices with respect to people with learning difficulties 3 A sound knowledge of, and commitment to Equal Opportunities issues and practices 4 Effective written and verbal communication skills 5 Effective administrative skills 6 Effective time management skills 7 Ability to manage and delegate work	1 Knowledge and experience of the implementation of disciplinary and grievance policies and procedures 2 Experience of working in a multi-ethnic environment 3 Familiarity with computerised management information systems
Disposition, personal qualities	1 Awareness of own strengths and weaknesses 2 Ability to cope with stress and pressure 3 Good sense of humour 4 Professional integrity 5 Ability to work in a team	
Circumstances	1 Ability to undertake on-call duties 2 Ability to undertake shift work, weekend and evening work	

Person Specification – Care Assistant

	Essential	Desirable
Qualifications	Completed secondary school education	GCE/GCSE/CSE to grades D or 2, including English
Work experience	Evidence of reliability through work experience, whether paid or unpaid, formal or informal	Experience in a care environment

▶

Person Specification – Care Assistant (Continued)

	Essential	Desirable
Skills, abilities, knowledge	1 Effective written and oral communication skills 2 Ability to listen effectively 3 Ability to undertake basic practical tasks competently	Experience of specific care tasks, such as helping people with eating, continence and dressing
Disposition, personal qualities	1 Ability to get on with older people 2 Ability to cope with variable pressures 3 Good sense of humour 4 Ability to work in a team 5 Honesty	Enthusiasm for a career in the caring services
Circumstances	1 Ability to undertake shift duties (day) and to work at weekends 2 Ability to climb stairs	Ability to undertake night shifts

Advertising the post

Having decided that a post needs to be filled, the next task is to publicise it. This is more than simply placing an advertisement in a newspaper. You may have informal links with likely sources of recruits and you should exploit these as far as possible. Job centres and other agencies can also be used.

In some cases, existing staff working elsewhere in the organisation might be interested in the job; if this is the case, an internal advert might prove fruitful. Details should be circulated in newsletters or similar publications. Larger organisations usually have policies about which types of posts can be filled internally and which must be advertised externally.

If external advertising is needed, local advertising is often the most cost effective. In some cases, advertising in national newspapers or professional journals is justified. Wherever they are placed, advertisements should be eye-catching and to the point. They should emphasise the key message and need not go into great detail because enquirers will be sent an information pack about the post. If possible, include interview dates in the advertisement.

ACTIVITY

Collect a number of local and national newspapers and professional journals. Examine the job adverts carefully.

- Which adverts caught your eye? Why was this?
- Choose one of the existing jobs in your own place of employment, or identify a possible new one. Draft an advertisement for this job.
- Discuss this draft with colleagues. Compare your views about what makes an effective advertisement?

Information about the post

Provide all enquirers with adequate information about the post. Information packs will vary but they usually include:

- a personal and welcoming letter, including a contact name and an offer to visit informally;
- job description;
- person specification;
- application form and any supplements, such as an ethnic monitoring form, medical questionnaire and declaration of criminal convictions/consent to a police check; application forms ask for data relating to qualifications, experience, past employment and for a 'letter of application' setting out the reasons for applying for this post; applicants will also be asked for details of two, sometimes three, people who can be asked for references;
- background to the post and the organisation as a whole, for example nursery provision, access to buildings (such as ramps and lifts);

conditions of service (hours of work, shift systems, wages, holidays, sickness pay); staff development opportunities;
- local information – housing, amenities, attractions;
- equal opportunities policy and details of how this is monitored;
- other relevant policies, for example sexual harassment.

Give applicants the opportunity to make informal visits because they can provide a much clearer idea of what is required in the job. However, the ability to arrange an informal visit should not give an applicant an unfair advantage. There are many good reasons why applicants cannot visit – for instance the applicant's present employer may not allow the time off, travel time might be excessive or too expensive, or child care may be impossible to arrange.

9.2 Selecting staff

Devising a selection procedure

The selection procedure should be worked out well in advance. Even where a standard pattern has been used several times before, it's always worth reviewing whether the approach suits this particular post.

Shortlisting

The timetable for selection should state when shortlisting will take place and who will decide the shortlist. Inform shortlisted candidates as soon as possible to allow them the maximum time to prepare for the interview day.

A typical application consists of:

- a covering letter;
- a completed application form;
- a curriculum vitae (possibly).

You should assess each application against the person specification. If there is a large number of applications, use a checklist and make brief notes on each applicant under the main headings taken from the person specification. Some people like to score each section, for example out of 10. If you use a scoring system, be sure to go back over the applications quickly a second time and adjust scores if necessary. After reading through many application forms, you will find it very difficult to maintain the same standards of scoring; you don't want a change in your standards to penalise applicants.

Some applications will be rejected quite quickly because they cannot meet the essential criteria, such as appropriate qualifications. Shortlisting often needs several stages during which applications will be rejected until you have reached the agreed number for the shortlist. For most posts this is usually between three and five. Fewer than this and the choice is generally too limited; more and the process becomes unwieldy. However, this is not an absolute rule and, for some posts, there may be very good reasons to vary it. You may need to accept a shortlist of two, or even one, when posts are hard to fill.

Your response to applications will be influenced by various factors, for example:

- the overall appearance of the application form;
- handwriting or quality of typing;
- spelling;

- whether instructions have been followed;
- whether all sections have been completed;
- the tone of the application, for example does the applicant sell her/ himself well?
- what is the evidence that an applicant can grow into the post – in other words what is his /her potential?

Be careful to assess fairly – avoid being too hard or too soft. Remember also that shortlisting is only one stage and that each part of the person specification will be considered again during the interview day.

> **ACTIVITY**
>
> Think back to when you were interviewed for your present post. Try to recall the anxieties and concerns you had.
>
> - What lessons did you learn from your personal experience?
> - How well do you think the suggested interview day for the Assistant Manager's post meets the needs of applicants? How well does it meet the needs of the organisation; for example does it give adequate opportunity to consider the items in the person specification?
> - What changes would you make to this programme?

Planning the interview day

The programme for the day should be sent well in advance to shortlisted candidates so that they can begin to prepare. An interview day for the assistant manager's post mentioned earlier might look like this:

Eastly House
Assistant Manager Interviews
Programme for the Day

09.30	Arrive at Eastly House Coffee with the Manager, Mrs Heidi Palmer, in the staff room.
10.00	Informal discussion about the post with Heidi Palmer and the Personnel Manager, Mr Mukesh Gunnoo.
11.00	Meet with residents of Eastly House over coffee.
11.45	Meet with staff of Eastly House and see the facilities.
12.30	Buffet lunch. As soon as lunch is over you will have approximately one hour 'free time'. Please feel free to spend this as you wish.
14.30	Individual interviews. The interviewing panel will be: Heidi Palmer Mukesh Gunnoo Alison Medici, Principal Officer.

Interviewing

The most common form of interview is the panel interview in which a single interviewee is interviewed by a panel of interviewers. Panel members take turns to ask questions, usually in a predetermined sequence. You should conduct an interview in a fairly informal manner. There is no excuse for uncomfortable chairs or panel members lined up as in a firing squad. A more relaxed style does not make the interview any less rigorous or demanding; it just reduces unnecessary strain.

The interview room should be comfortable and quiet, and a waiting room with adequate privacy made available to candidates. While they are waiting, always offer candidates tea or coffee. Tell them also where they can find the toilets and where they can smoke.

Prior to the start of the interview, the panel members should agree the areas of questioning and who will take responsibility for each. This helps to ensure that the interview is conducted within the letter and spirit of equal opportunities legislation and organisational policies. Panel members should point out any worries that they have about the application form – discrepancies or contradictions, for instance – which can then be dealt with in the interview.

Always do your homework before the panel meets for the first time. Select areas you would like to ask about and put these forward. It's a good idea to prepare more questions than you will have time to ask. Write your questions out in full, especially if you are new to interviewing. You don't have to keep to the exact wording each time but having a 'script' ready will reduce your anxiety. Keep the structure of your questions as simple as possible. Many poor interviewers 'wander' when asking a question and succeed only in confusing candidates as well as themselves and their colleagues. This is unprofessional and inconsiderate to candidates and can be avoided by careful preparation.

Make notes on each candidate at the time of the interview. Most interviewers write brief notes immediately after asking their questions. Complete your notes before the next candidate arrives. Even with only three or four candidates, it is surprising how quickly your memory will start to fade.

Making a decision

When all the interviews have been completed, the chairperson of the panel will guide the members towards a decision. Be prepared to put your independent point of view. Do not feel intimidated because of the personalities involved or because you might be junior to the others present. The person appointed may well be your colleague in the very near future and your views matter. The panel will base its decision on several sources of evidence:

- the interview;
- the selection day events;
- information in the application form;
- references.

There are three common ways of informing candidates of the result of their applications:

1 immediately, in person, at the end of the selection day; this requires all candidates to stay until the very end of the process;

Choosing the best person for the job

2 by telephone on the same or the following day;
3 by letter.

Whatever the method, always offer unsuccessful candidates the chance to discuss why they were not selected. The panel should decide in advance who will take responsibility for this. Treat unsuccessful candidates with tact and honesty. If the shortlisting process was done well, then all candidates started with a chance of getting the job. Keep comments objective and avoid expressing too much sympathy – it often makes the person feel even worse! If the person seems receptive, indicate areas which can be worked on for future occasions – the need to gain specific professional experience or improvements in interview technique, for example. If the disappointment is too great, offer to give feedback at a later date.

9.3 Equal opportunities

Every organisation and each employee concerned with any aspect of recruitment and selection should support the philosophy of equal opportunities and be aware of their legal obligations. The caring professions are rightly proud of the fact that they aim to treat clients with respect, dignity and individuality. It follows, therefore, that these values should also underpin the way in which staff are treated.

In general, it is unlawful to discriminate against people on the grounds of:

- race, colour, nationality or ethnic origin;
- sex and marital status;
- a past criminal conviction which is now 'spent';
- being or not being a member of a trade union;
- religion (Northern Ireland).

However, there are certain exceptions to these. For instance, the Rehabilitation of Offenders Act 1974 does not apply to staff in the care field. Consequently, applicants must declare all convictions however long ago they occurred. Also, as mentioned in Chapter 3, it can be legal to discriminate in favour of a particular racial group if that group is considered to be 'a genuine occupational qualification' (GOQ).

Avoiding unlawful discrimination in recruitment and selection is not a once-and-for-all action. It needs constant vigilance and systematic monitoring. Here are some key points:

- adverts should be structured to avoid all discriminatory wording (except for GOCs);
- where illustrated brochures are used, they should depict both sexes, different racial groups, disabled employees, employees of different ages;
- process all applications in the same way – for example don't separate married and unmarried, or men and women;
- ensure that exactly the same conditions are offered to all candidates for a job – for example pay, holidays;
- avoid creating conditions which favour a particular group – for example specifying a particular age range may discriminate against women of child-bearing age;
- check that the criteria in the person specification are all necessary; for instance, demands for lengthy and continuous periods of specific kinds of past employment may discriminate against women;

- ensure that educational qualifications are reasonable and not excessive – particularly important in respect of command of English; the key criteria are safety and competence in the job;
- avoid selection tests which contain activities or questions demanding knowledge or experience unfamiliar to particular racial groups, unless this knowledge and experience is crucial to the requirements of the job;
- at interview, treat all candidates in the same way; don't bias the questioning according to sex, race or other personal characteristics of the candidate.

9.4 Induction of new staff

Induction begins the moment a job has been offered. Arguably, it has already started when the applicant first reads the job advertisement. At that moment the potential new employee begins to learn about the organisation and the post.

Aim to provide written induction material before new members of staff take up post. This enables them to prepare and to have some questions ready for later. Many organisations have a standard induction programme which can be added to depending on the post. Because the induction contains critically important information, both you and the new recruit should sign to confirm that induction has taken place.

You should create an induction programme which incorporates the following components. It should aim to introduce the person to:

- the client group;
- specific responsibilities of the job;
- the organisation as a whole;
- health and safety matters;
- special hazards or requirements.

ACTIVITY

Recall your own induction programme.

- Were you satisfied? Did it give you what you needed?
- If not, identify where improvements should have been made.
- How do you carry out inductions at the moment? Have you learned the lessons from your own experiences?

Induction takes time

The length of induction depends on the type of post – from a single day to several weeks. Don't present induction as a rush job, as a bureaucratic necessity to be over and done with as soon as possible. If time is short – often the case in care work – then spread the process out over a longer period. Decide on priorities: some things need to be covered at once, others can wait.

ACTIVITY

This is an induction schedule designed to meet the needs of a small residential care home for people with mental health problems. It covers three shifts and aims to ensure that new care assistants are safe with clients and are beginning to feel confident in their role.

- Do you think the schedule is able to achieve these aims?
- Would you see any problems in implementing it?
- What improvements would you suggest?

INDUCTION OF NEW STAFF

Name of staff member:
Date of appointment:

CHECKLIST Tick

Topics and procedures to be introduced during the first day:

- *introduction to residents* ____
- *layout of the building* ____
- *fire system and evacuation procedure* ____
- *health and safety* ____
- *food hygiene and handling* ____
- *where to find information* ____
- *rights of each resident* ____
- *answering the telephone* ____
- *reporting and recording* ____
- *introduction to the general needs of these client groups* ____

Signature of supervisor ....

Signature of staff member ....

Every care assistant will be competent in the following areas within the stated periods:

Signatures:

Supervisor *Staff*

By the end of the first shift:

How to get help in an emergency;
How to raise the fire alarm;
How to evacuate residents in the event of fire;

Comments:

Date: ....

ACTIVITY (Continued)

By the end of the third shift:

Know all residents' names and how they like to be addressed;
Know the location of each resident's room;
Demonstrate awareness of the importance of the residents' Charter of Rights;
Start positive relationships with clients;
Begin to feel part of the staff team;
Be familiar with the following policies:

- *admission and discharge*
- *complaints*
- *disciplinary and grievance*
- *health and safety.*

Apply the principles of safe lifting;
Write an accurate entry in the daily record book.

Comments

Date: ....

Reading on...

★ Employment law is very complex and you should always refer to a reliable source, such as: *Croner's Employment Law*, Croner Publications Ltd.
★ For more information about Croner Publications, contact Croner House, London Road, Kingston-upon-Thames, Surrey KT2 6SR. Tel. 0181 547 3333.

10 Developing staff

We are learning all the time, whether or not we are aware of it. However, effective learning takes time, effort and organisation. This applies to your own learning and development, as well as to that of your staff. Learning in the workplace can be especially hard because of the pressures of the job. Nevertheless, workplace learning can be a great motivator because of its relevance to the job.

This chapter is about how you can meet your training and development responsibilities towards both your staff and yourself. It covers a wide range of development activities, including:

- creating a learning climate;
- why people learn;
- planning learning and teaching;
- induction;
- vocational qualifications (for example NVQ, SVQ);
- staff appraisal;
- professional supervision;
- self development.

10.1 Creating a learning environment

You must encourage staff to keep up-to-date, to gain the skills necessary to provide high quality, sensitive care, and to value learning for its own sake. People who value learning in this way are more inclined to take responsibility for their own learning. Because the care sector is changing rapidly, staff at all levels need to question existing practice, explore and share possible alternatives and try out new approaches.

ACTIVITY

Be a good example to your team. A negative or contrived attitude to learning will show up badly and encourage cynicism. Ask yourself the following questions:

- Do I take a genuine interest in my own learning needs?
- How do I show my staff that I am interested in learning?
- How often do I raise the issue of learning in the course of my everyday work?
- Do I challenge staff and colleagues if they suggest that learning is 'pointless', ' a waste of time' or 'unnecessary, because you can't teach an old dog new tricks!'.
- Do I encourage team members to take the lead in teaching in the workplace?

10.2 Why people learn

The benefits of learning to the individual go well beyond acquiring new knowledge or skills. Learning also raises self-esteem, instils greater confidence and creates a stronger sense of purpose.

Keep the following general principles in mind whenever you are organising learning in the workplace.

Purpose

Learning needs direction and purpose. Good workplace learning exploits the features of the job and is related to the career expectations of staff. Consider the following questions:

- How is learning linked to client or patient needs and to improvements in care?
- How will learning help the individual staff member, either as preparation for promotion, or for further learning or personal growth?
- How will it meet the needs of the organisation?

If you plan learning activities which fail to produce positive answers to these questions, think again.

Relevance

Keep learning relevant to the workplace. Learning is most effective when it starts from the real needs of clients or patients, and the efforts of carers to satisfy these needs. Learning then becomes a natural process through which experiences are shared and greater understanding developed.

Don't over-emphasise the 'academic' components of learning. Some people behave as if learning must be 'difficult' – for example, by insisting on using language which is unnecessarily complicated. Effective learning always stretches the mind, of course, and sometimes this can be uncomfortable. Despite this, even the most complex ideas can be explained in clear, simple language.

Rewards

We all need rewards from time to time. However, some of the most powerful are social rather than material. Most of us are susceptible to the more subtle influences of social approval and praise. Make sure you acknowledge the achievements of your staff as they develop new skills and competencies.

Curiosity

Learning should stimulate our natural curiosity. Learning can be infectious and addictive – in this case, happily, an addiction which can be encouraged. Behind this natural curiosity are some very serious motives, however: to make more sense of the world and to feel in control of events.

Build on existing knowledge and skills

Many staff have a lot of experience and knowledge about their present jobs and about caring in general. Respect your staff by recognising this and by using this knowledge for the benefit of the whole team. Remember that staff are also adults with valuable life experiences that you can draw on to get staff involved and interested in their own learning.

10.3 Planning learning and teaching

Learning is a continual process and can happen by accident or by design. Contrary to what many educators would like to think, much significant learning occurs spontaneously. For example, most of us can remember experiences with particular clients or colleagues which were critical in shaping our personal beliefs and attitudes towards caring.

ACTIVITY

1 Spend a few moments reflecting on your early experiences in care work. Take particular note of the people who begin to feature in these memories. Most of us can recall 'special' clients or colleagues who were important to us. From my own experience, I have very clear memories of :

- working with a colleague who provided care by challenging clients (not the stereotypical 'caring' person at all!);
- the first time I had to cope with the death of a patient;
- getting to know a young girl of my own age who had a chronic, terminal illness.
- the first time I had to take disciplinary action against a member of my team.

2 Make a list of your own and ask yourself what it was you learned from these experiences. This is a totally personal exercise and only you will know what you learned. On the other hand, this kind of learning is often the most influential because it can be so intense and so enduring.

However, a considerable amount of learning can be planned because it covers skills and knowledge known to be important in providing high quality care.

Assessing learning needs

All organised learning in the workplace should start from an assessment of the learning needs of staff. In deciding what is relevant, you need to take into account several factors, some of which are national, others local, such as:

- national policies – for example the drive towards care in the community and the commitment to a national framework of vocational qualifications;
- expectations of local statutory agencies – such as purchasing authorities and inspection units.
- the philosophy, mission statement, aims and objectives of your organisation;
- the training policy of your organisation;
- the type of clients you are catering for; individual clients and their needs;
- job descriptions of staff;
- the present levels of knowledge and skills in the team;
- the ambitions and aspirations of staff.

Learning needs can be specific to one individual or they may be common to several members of staff. For instance, you may have a team member who has not yet had the opportunity to learn how to prepare a discharge plan for a client. An *individual training plan* can then be agreed with that person which might include:

- a discussion with a member of staff experienced in writing and implementing discharge plans;
- observing this person preparing a client and his family for discharge;
- the opportunity to carry out the process personally, though under supervision.

The aim is to get the person to an appropriate level of competence in a logical and efficient way. You need to ensure also that the learning activity is recorded – this could form part of a portfolio in which training activities are documented.

ACTIVITY

1 Does your place of work have a training, or staff development, policy? If not, try persuading your manager that it is an idea worth looking at. Most policies include statements on each of the following:
- induction training for new staff ;
- continuing education and training;
- support for staff attending courses;
- target qualifications and training according to job roles;
- in-house learning opportunities and resources.

2 Does your own policy cover these areas? If there is no training policy where you work, think about what policy statements you would like to see under each of these headings.

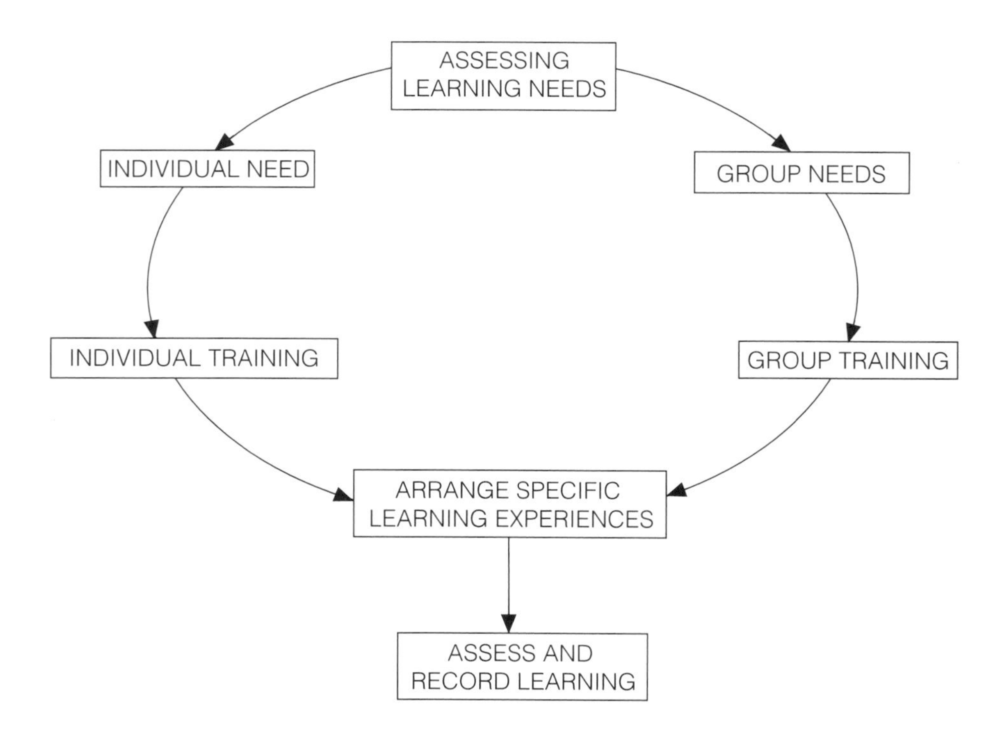

Continuing the example given above, what if discharge plans are new to the whole organisation? In this case, you could devise a *group training programme*, involving all staff – it would make good educational and economic sense.

You should aim to compare the current abilities of each member of staff with the demands made by the job. This comparison has to be systematic, of course, and is usually based on an assessment of current, and likely future, responsibilities.

Where a thorough assessment of learning needs is required – perhaps as part of a formal staff appraisal – you will need to use a structured checklist to collect the information. The checklist below has been adapted from an example given in Douglas and Payne (1988).

CHECKLIST

Assessment of individual learning needs

Name:

Date:

- Personal details (for example sex, ethnicity, religion, union affiliation):
- Previous general education and training:
- Previous professional education and training (including in-house, external courses at local institutions and by distance learning):
- Length of service and career pattern:
- Career aspirations and expectations:
- Description of present role and how this relates to formal job description:
- Specific key tasks for which further training is required:
- Other significant factors influencing the work, for example stress levels, peer support:
- Self-assessment of learning needs (by member of staff):
- Extent to which learning needs are shared with other staff:
- Summary of training needs in priority order:
- Action plan indicating who will do what and by when:

Agreed by:

Member of staff .... Supervisor ....

Implementing learning programmes

Learning can occur in numerous ways and in many settings. Douglas and Payne (1988) have provided a helpful framework for analysing the range of learning opportunities. These opportunities can vary in three ways. They can be:

1 formal or informal;
2 on site or off site;
3 individual or group.

I have adapted Douglas and Payne's ideas as follows:

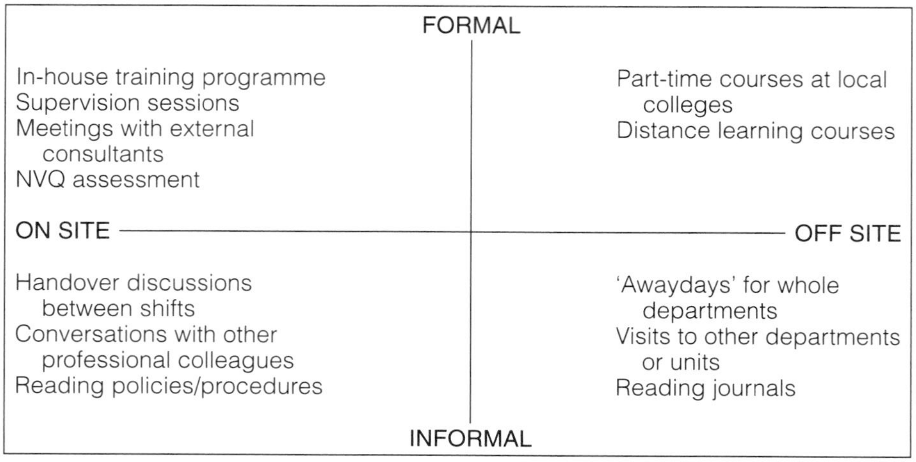

	FORMAL	
ON SITE	In-house training programme Supervision sessions Meetings with external consultants NVQ assessment	OFF SITE
	Part-time courses at local colleges Distance learning courses	

	Formal	Informal
ON SITE	In-house training programme Supervision sessions Meetings with external consultants NVQ assessment	Handover discussions between shifts Conversations with other professional colleagues Reading policies/procedures
OFF SITE	Part-time courses at local colleges Distance learning courses	'Awaydays' for whole departments Visits to other departments or units Reading journals

Types of learning activity

10.4 Helping staff learn

There are specific skills and methods you can use to help staff in their workplace learning. If you want to develop these skills further, you should contact your local college of further education and ask about appropriate courses and qualifications, such as those offered by the City and Guilds of London Institute. Your employer may organise in-house courses in teaching and learning.

Some of the most important skills and methods are as follows:

Explanation

Clear explanations are an essential part of effective teaching and learning. If you have ever had to listen to muddled explanations, you will not wish to inflict this on others. To explain effectively:

- decide what you want to explain – identify key concepts;
- organise the material into an appropriate sequence;
- use relevant examples;
- speak clearly;
- give enough time;
- use uncomplicated language – avoid jargon;
- use diagrams where appropriate;
- repeat main points;
- summarise the main points at the end;
- check that the person has understood.

Effective explanation is important in many aspects of your work, both formal and informal, such as when you have to make a presentation (see the section on 'oral presentation' in Chapter 5).

Skills teaching

One of your regular tasks will be to ensure that staff are able to learn specific skills, such as how to:

- help children to use certain play materials;
- give an injection;
- help an elderly person with Alzheimer's disease to dress;
- facilitate a group discussion.

Although skills vary greatly in complexity, teaching any skill involves a number of stages:

1. Demonstrate the whole skill yourself while the member of staff observes.
2. Analyse the skill into its component parts, in other words sub-skills, that the member of staff can cope with at one at a time. A sub-skill might be drawing up a liquid into a syringe or opening a discussion group.
3. Ask the member of staff to practise the skill, or sub-skill, while you observe.
4. Give helpful comments so that the member of staff can improve performance.
5. You should repeat the demonstration as necessary, in full or in part.
6. You should take every opportunity to encourage appropriate performance at every stage.

Because individuals will learn skills at their own speeds, you need to show patience as well as persistence.

Role play

> **ACTIVITY**
>
> Can you think of situations in your own place of work where you could use role play to help learning? List some of these and then try to work out how you would put them into practice.

A good way to learn how to be a better carer is to understand how it feels to be the client. By using role play, you can often get across important points that are almost impossible to make through words alone. It is also an excellent way of developing your own reflective practice skills and those of your staff (see Chapter 3). An example will show how you could use role play:

> *You want to show Irene, a new care assistant, how best to help a client who has lost the use of his left arm due to a stroke. You ask Irene to play the part of the client and to pretend to be unable to use her left arm. You then help her to put on a cardigan. When you have finished, ask Irene what it felt like to be 'disabled' in this way, how it affected her expectations and so on.*
>
> *After this, you ask Irene to be herself while you play the client. Irene then helps you to put on the cardigan. If the role play has been effective, Irene will be more able to anticipate your needs and make a better job of helping with the cardigan.*

Of course, you would not use role play on its own. You still need to explain the principles behind the care activity but role play gives a sense of reality not achievable by any other means of teaching.

You also need to be careful in choosing appropriate situations. If you select a very emotive topic, for example how to deal with a bereaved relative, you may find that the role playing touches closely the personal feelings of the participants. If this happens, always give plenty of opportunity for all participants to talk about their experiences afterwards. If you are unsure of your ability to cope with emotions released in this way, you might decide to stick to more practical topics such as the example given above.

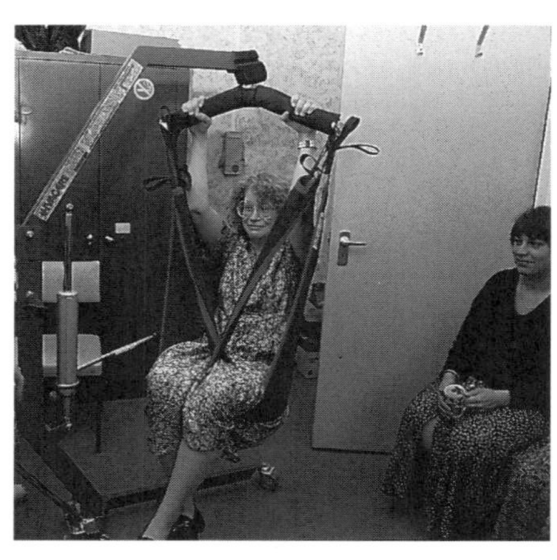
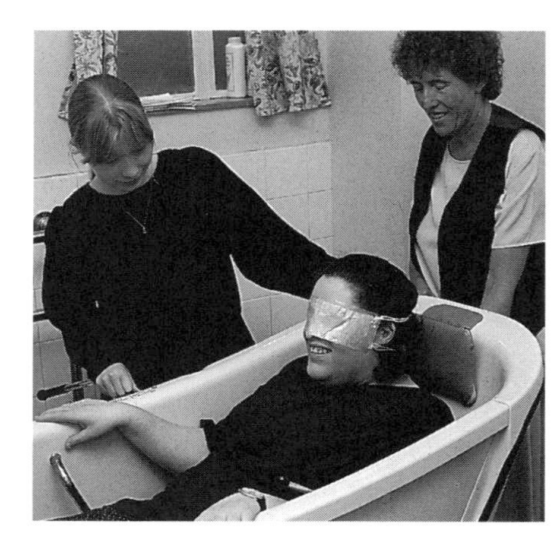

Learning through role play

Coaching

Coaching goes beyond the teaching and learning of a specific skill. It is a method used to help a person to be more effective in their role. Someone may become technically competent in a set of skills through formal training courses, for example, but struggle to apply these in practice. New staff are often in this position.

Coaching is usually carried out by the line manager working *with* a member of staff. Although you may not be greatly involved in formal training, you will almost certainly find opportunities to coach staff. Effective coaching depends on:

- accurate observation and analysis of the performance of staff;
- understanding the needs of individual members of staff at particular times – thinking back to your own past experiences can help you in this;
- linking these needs with those of the organisation, so that the organisation's objectives are not ignored – coaching is about effective performance; it is not counselling;
- setting realistic aims – don't expect too much too soon;
- giving the responsibility for learning and improvement to individuals, so that they maintain self-esteem and take personal satisfaction in their progress;
- providing opportunities when necessary; for example, you may be able to arrange access to a useful person or situation, perhaps a visit to another unit to get fresh ideas;

> **ACTIVITY**
>
> Sunil had just completed his Project 2000 Nursing Diploma. His performance as a student had been outstanding, both academically and during his placements in clinical areas. However, in his first post as a qualified nurse working in the community mental health team, he felt 'all at sea'. He began to have doubts about his competence, even his choice of career.
>
> - As his immediate manager, how would you deal with Sunil's problems?
> - What do you think would be most helpful – coaching, shadowing, mentoring, or a combination?
> - How would you prioritise your actions?
> - Have you ever felt like this yourself? How did you overcome the problem?

- giving feedback – this should be as precise as possible, objective and with the emphasis on future action; be generous with your praise when improvements have occurred.

Mentoring

Mentoring is a broader approach to learning than coaching, and is based on a particular kind of relationship. A mentor helps a member of staff to learn and develop by acting as a support and guide. She or he is someone who can be used to clarify issues and give advice. Compared to the person being mentored, the mentor is more knowledgeable and experienced, usually older and often of the same gender. He or she should be able to respond to the needs of the individual as and when required.

You may wish to establish a mentoring relationship for a new member of staff, perhaps for the first six months or year. You might be the mentor yourself or you might choose another experienced member of your team.

If you work in a situation where students are allocated for training purposes, you may already be familiar with this kind of mentoring. In these cases, mentors are often a critical link between the workplace and the university or college responsible for organising the training course.

Shadowing

Valuable learning can be achieved by closely observing an experienced person at work over a planned period of time – a few days or a week perhaps. This is known as shadowing. For example, an occupational therapist working in a hospital unit will better understand the needs of her clients if she can shadow the work of a community occupational therapist.

Coaching helps staff to apply skills in practice

Making material resources available

Material resources can assist workplace learning. These can include professional magazines and journals, textbooks, equipment catalogues; college and university prospectuses and open learning materials.

You can also create 'resource files' that you maintain to meet your own specific needs. These can be in the form of information written on index cards housed in their own box. Information of this kind can also be stored on a computer database for speedy access. Alternatively, a much wider range of information can be collected if you use an 'open file' system, using a filing cabinet or cardboard wallets. The advantage of these is that you can include leaflets, booklets, notes made by members of staff and cuttings from newspapers and magazines. This is a very flexible method because all staff can add to, and access, the store of information, and it can be kept up-to-date at minimal cost. With care practices and approaches changing regularly, a flexible system is a great advantage.

10.5 Vocational qualifications

As explained in the first chapter, the content of this book will provide you with a sound basis for supervisory management practice, including the occupational standards for managers, developed by the Management Charter Initiative (MCI). These standards form the basis of National Vocational Qualifications (NVQ) and Scottish Vocational Qualifications (SVQ) offered by various Awarding Bodies, such as the Business and Technology Education Council (BTEC). NVQ/SVQs are offered in many different occupational areas at five different levels (1–5). Not every area has awards at all five levels.

There are several NVQ/SVQs in the health and care fields, for example:

- *Level 3:*
  - acute care
  - clinic and out-patient care
  - mental health care
  - mobility and movement
  - terminal care
  - child care and education (family day care)
  - health care – physiological measurement (audiology);

- *Level 2:*
  - residential/hospital support
  - special care needs
  - domiciliary support
  - child care and education (work with babies).

If you are responsible for staff not in the care field, you should obtain information about the NVQ/SVQs which might apply to them. For instance, there are qualifications in catering and business administration.

The value of NVQ/SVQs

In a recent survey, a wide range of employers reported the following benefits of NVQs:

- improvements in productivity;
- increases in market share;
- improvements in the quality of work;
- increased profitability;
- improved customer service;
- reductions in staff turnover and absenteeism.

Source: Paul Ellis (1995) *The 1995 NVQ Criteria and Guidance, in Competence and Assessment*, published by the Employment Department, pp. 2–4

Your role in NVQ/SVQ

NVQ/SVQs are based on competence in the workplace. Candidates submit evidence and claim competence. Evidence can be in several forms, such as direct observation by an assessor either in the workplace or in simulated conditions, written evidence or oral questioning. As far as the care qualifications are concerned, most of the assessment should take place at work. In other cases, such as catering, much of the assessment can take place in colleges or other training units where they have kitchens and training restaurants.

Before your staff can benefit from Care NVQ/SVQs, your organisation has to be an approved Assessment Centre in its own right or be part of a consortium. Awarding bodies, such as BTEC, City and Guilds or CCETSW, provide this approval if the Assessment Centre meets a set of strict

NVQ assessment in practice

conditions. One of these conditions is that there should be enough appropriately qualified workplace assessors. The work of the assessors is monitored by Internal Verifiers appointed by the Assessment Centre. With other NVQ/SVQs, staff will be able to take their qualifications through a college that is an Assessment Centre. NVQ/SVQ candidates have to register with an awarding body through an Assessment Centre; they cannot register directly with the awarding body. This is because the work of the assessment centre has to be monitored by an External Verifier appointed by the awarding body. External Verifiers visit assessment centres to ensure that national standards are being maintained by the workplace assessors and the Internal Verifiers.

To be fully involved in NVQ/SVQs, you should consider qualifying as a workplace assessor. You are then able to assess the competence of your staff when they are registered for NVQ/SVQs. The assessor standards are themselves part of the NVQ/SVQ system and were created by the Training and Development Lead Body (TDLB); these qualifications are awarded by several bodies, including BTEC, City and Guilds, the Royal Society of Arts (RSA) and the Institute of Training and Development. There are two Units especially designed for assessors: D32 (Assess candidate performance) and D33 (Assess candidate using differing sources of evidence). Together these Units cover the competencies needed to assess candidates by direct observations and by examining different kinds of evidence such as reports, records and portfolios.

The NVQ/SVQ system is complex and if you are interested in getting involved personally or to provide guidance for your staff, you should obtain information from the NCVQ or the awarding bodies. Details are given in Appendix 1. You can also find out more from your training unit (if there is one in your organisation) or by approaching a local College of Further Education. Colleges usually offer a variety of NVQ/SVQ training opportunities, including assessor training.

10.6 Staff appraisal

Most large organisations operate formal systems of staff appraisal; smaller employers may have less formal arrangements but they still need to ensure that their employees are performing to a satisfactory standard. In some areas, the term individual performance review (IPR) is used instead of appraisal.

When implemented effectively, appraisal is a valuable force for professional development.

Whatever the differences in detail, appraisal systems should:

- recognise strengths;
- identify areas for improvement and suggest actions;
- encourage trust and constructive self-criticism;
- set realistic targets, with appropriate support;
- reflect the range and complexity of individuals' roles;
- allow upward appraisal, namely the views of the appraisee on the appraisal process and on the organisation;
- be effective, efficient and as simple as possible.

Many staff have varied roles and appraisal should be able to take this into account. Poor systems often depend too heavily on the personal views of the line manager who may not always be aware of much of an appraisee's work. If important areas of evidence are missing, appraisal cannot be as fair as it should be and staff could feel, with some justification, that their hard work has gone unrecognised. This can be avoided by including a wider range of evidence, and by giving appraisees more control over the collection of this evidence.

One way of improving appraisal systems is to give more control to the appraisees. This can be done by ensuring that they can bring to the appraisal more complete evidence of their performance. A comprehensive system might include the following:

- self-assessment;
- evidence from colleagues;
- evidence from clients;
- line manager assessment.

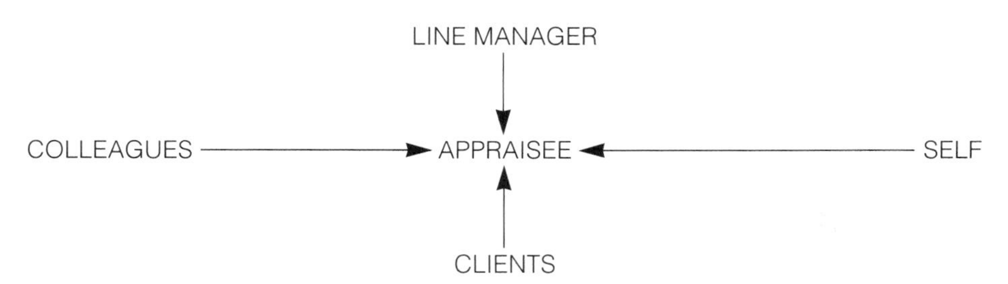

In a system which includes all of the above, the line manager's role changes from 'judge' to someone who collates evidence and manages the overall process. Staff are encouraged to gather evidence from a variety of sources and present this 'portfolio' to the line manager. Some systems include a 'grandparent' in the process – usually the appraiser's own line manager. This person oversees the process, perhaps interviews the appraisee briefly to check fairness and often adds written comments to the final document. Whether or not there is a grandparent role, every appraisal system must incorporate an appeals procedure so that appraisees have the chance to correct bias and prejudice if it is present.

Appraisal systems are usually carried out annually, or every two years with an interim review. In some organisations, annual appraisals would be too time-consuming or would not encourage appraisees to achieve longer-term targets.

The appraisal process often involves four key stages:

1. *Initial interview* – to review targets set at the last appraisal and to agree the evidence to be collected.
2. *Evidence collection and presentation* – undertaken by the appraisee after agreement with the appraiser.

ACTIVITY

1 Alison supervises a small team of community nurses in a rural area. Although she prides herself on her ability to keep in touch with the work of her colleagues, she knows that there are important parts of their roles that she knows next to nothing about, for example, their links with local GP practices, relationships with hospital colleagues, even the one-to-one care provided for clients. The appraisal system in operation requires her to make annual judgements on the performance of each team member. The documents she has to complete only allow her to rank the importance of different activities and then to rate these and make comments. For instance, for the category 'establishes effective relationships with patients and their families', she has to

- decide whether this is a high, medium or low priority activity;
- rate the performance of the appraisee on a scale of 1 to 4 (1 indicating 'excellent').

For some time Alison has felt concerned about making these judgements. The members of her team seem to find the whole system irrelevant, saying 'It's just a paper exercise. I can't see the value' and 'It does nothing for me!'.

The Trust is about to evaluate the current appraisal system and she would like to suggest ways of improving the system.

2 Do you share Alison's concerns?
How would you suggest she could make the existing system work better?
What changes would you like to see made to this system?

3. *Final interview* – between line manager and appraisee to review the evidence and discuss performance; to set new targets, agree an action plan and to identify training needs.
4. *Preparation of the final appraisal documentation* – drafted by the line manager and commented on by the appraisee.

Appraisers and appraisees will not always agree. If, after carrying out the process fairly and competently, they cannot reach agreement, then the appraiser's conclusions will have to be recorded. However, appraisees should always have the right to formally express their disagreement in writing on the final appraisal form. Where there are serious disagreements which appraisees feel are due to personal prejudice or incompetence on the part of the appraiser, this should be dealt with through the appeals procedure.

Because the responsibility for conducting the appraisal interviews and for preparing the documentation usually falls to the immediate line manager, you need to feel confident in your ability to manage the process. Most organisations will require training of appraisers, usually in-house. Justified or not, most employees regard appraisal with some degree of anxiety and you have a responsibility to your staff to prepare yourself well.

10.7 Professional supervision

Many care organisations recognise the benefits of formal professional supervision. Historically, social work has been committed to the practice of supervision for a considerable time. Other professions and occupations have been slower to adopt it but this is changing. For example, the Department of Health has recently endorsed the idea of 'clinical supervision' for all nurses. A recent Department of Health document includes the following:

> 'Clinical supervision is a formal process of professional support and learning which allows individual practitioners to develop knowledge and competence and assume responsibility for their own practice... Through supervision, theory and practice are brought together with the management and administrative requirement of health care provision... Supervisors are... expert nurses experienced in the same field of nursing as those receiving supervision.'

Professional supervision sets out to enhance the quality of the care provided to clients by:

- respecting care workers as individuals and acknowledging their professional needs;
- recognising their unique experiences, personal and cultural qualities and strengths;
- recognising the importance of open communication;
- instilling a sense of individual responsibility and accountability.

Supervision aims to improve practice by giving staff the opportunity to reflect on their work through regular meetings with an experienced colleague, usually the line manager. Professional supervision should be part of regular everyday work. By contrast, other opportunities for development and learning, such as coaching or mentoring, are shorter term activities.

Although individual supervision is common, some organisations offer group supervision as well. This might be the case where group work is a key part of the culture, for example in a community mental health team. In these situations, it may be very valuable for staff to share experiences and provide mutual support in groups.

Managing supervision

Good practice includes the following:

- Agree when, where and how long sessions will be and keep to this;
- Organise a room which is private and free from interruptions;
- Allow sufficient time for each session – some authorities advise sessions as long as 2 hours but, in most busy workplaces, this is unrealistic. However, anything less than half an hour is probably too short, however, because both staff and supervisor need enough time to switch to a more reflective mode of thinking;
- Decide on the balance between group and individual supervision. Some organisations make group supervision compulsory and individual supervision optional; others adopt the opposite approach;
- Plan sessions well ahead and programme them into your diary;
- Decide on areas for discussion. These could include:
  - general review of the work done since the last supervision session;
  - specific feedback on critical tasks or responsibilities;

Professional supervision in practice

- workload and how to deal with stresses of the job – sources of support and so on;
- any emerging training or professional development needs;
- individual issues which the member of staff wishes to raise;
- agreement on tasks/targets for next period.

Documenting supervision

There are several options:

- Use general checklists to guide sessions;
- Record key issues raised;
- Record any agreed action;
- Use a contract, in other words the whole process is contained within a contract between supervisor and supervisee. The contract could cover such areas as:
  - the timing and frequency of meetings
  - the length of meetings
  - the type and extent of recording of sessions
  - agreed areas for discussion
  - an agreed statement of the content of sessions
  - agreed follow-up actions to sessions.

The skills of professional supervision

You need to draw a definite line between professional supervision and personal counselling. Some problems are beyond everyday workplace supervision and need more in-depth and prolonged attention. Even if you are a trained counsellor, the supervision session is unlikely to be the appropriate setting for personal counselling. If you experience these kinds of difficulties and dilemmas, you should discuss them with your own supervisor.

ACTIVITY

As a social worker in a rehabilitation unit for people with physical handicaps, you are responsible for the supervision of a team of four support workers. Tom is a member of this team and you have been offering him individual supervision for about six months. You are pretty pleased with how things have gone so far – Tom is an amiable colleague, always wants to please and you have grown to like him. In fact, it is sometimes hard to keep to the point during sessions because you often seem to get sidetracked on to other topics.

At the last session, Tom revealed to you that he has been having great difficulties in his marriage. He and his wife argue constantly, and occasionally he has slapped her on the arm. He says he wants to tell you more about his problems because you are the only person he trusts.

- How would such a request make you feel?
- How should you respond in this situation?
- What factors should you consider when deciding what to do?
- Should you deal with the problem on your own or discuss it with a colleague?
- How do you think this incident could change your relationship with Tom?

10.8 Self development

You have to look after your own needs as well as those of your staff. Your needs might be quite specific – perhaps updated knowledge or technical skills – or more general, such as leadership, communication or stress management skills. In some cases, your employer might have a policy that all managers undertake a specified management development programme, or perhaps become NVQ assessors.

Identifying and meeting your own learning needs

You can identify your own learning and development needs by:

- Reflecting on past experiences, such as:
  - a particular problem or error
  - feeling that you should be able to do better
  - the need to respond to changes
  - the need to prepare yourself for future developments
  - lack of confidence;
- Discussing your performance and aspirations during your own professional supervision sessions;
- Recognising and responding to organisational changes, such as:
  - revision of your job description
  - restructuring of the organisation
  - policy changes in the organisation.

When you have identified what you think are your most important learning needs, discuss these with your own manager. You may also need to talk to other key staff, for example the training officer, staff development officer, personnel manager, proprietor – it will depend on who can offer professional advice and on who holds the training budget.

Not all learning needs are met by spending large sums of money. Informal in-house training can cost very little – for instance by arranging to discuss a particular issue with a more experienced or knowledgeable colleague. Some needs will be best met by external, formal training. In these cases, you can approach a local college or university for advice and guidance.

Reading the professional journals and newspapers is also an excellent way of keeping abreast of training opportunities. Remember, it is your personal and professional responsibility to stay informed and up-to-date.

Reading on....

★ Connor, Anne and Black, Stewart (1994) *Performance Review and Quality in Social Care*, Jessica Kingsley Publishers, London. Chapters 4 and 5 deal with appraisal and supervision and provide a useful summary of the issues in the context of social care.

★ Douglas, R. and Payne, C. (1988) *Organising for learning*, National Institute for Social Work.

★ Rogers, Jenny (1989) *Adults Learning*, Open University Press, Milton Keynes.

★ The National Council for Vocational Qualifications (NCVQ) publishes many relevant documents. You should contact them for more information about the whole range of NVQ/SVQ. The Council can tell you about existing qualifications and those currently being developed. Their address is: NCVQ, 222 Euston Road, London NW1 2BZ. Tel: 0171 387 9898; Fax 0171 387 0978.

★ Further details of NVQ/SVQs and awarding bodies are given in Appendices 1 and 2.

11 Managing change

> 'There is a certain relief in change, even though it be from bad to worse ... it is often a comfort to shift one's position and be bruised in a new place.'
>
> Washington Irving

All organisations have to cope with a continuous process of change and development. Change has become the norm. While this may be accepted as inevitable, even desirable, you should not underestimate the consequences for individuals and organisations alike. You have a key role to play in helping staff adapt to changing circumstances. You need to be able to understand the forces at work so that you can support your staff through change.

Almost everyone, at some stage of her or his career, will experience organisational restructuring. For some, this will lead to promotion, enhanced status and a healthier bank balance. For others, quite the opposite. For many, there is just a sense of disorientation and unease while the new order becomes established. Even without externally imposed change, care work is notoriously stressful. The need to respond to change can be, for some, the final straw; for others, it is the stimulus which prises them out of a comfortable rut.

11.1 Attitudes to change

The success or failure of planned change depends to a large extent on the attitudes of the staff who are responsible for its implementation and on those who are on the receiving end. Everyday experience tells us that people differ in their ability to cope with change – some relish the opportunity, others do all they can to maintain the status quo. Most of us are somewhere in between.

Although you cannot change another person's basic attitudes, you can supply the conditions in which all members of your team are able to express their views, test out new methods and share experiences. In this way, you will be doing all that is practicable to encourage an open-minded view towards the possibility of change.

11.2 Sources of change

Changes affecting your area of work result from either external or internal influences.

Examples of external forces include:

- policy changes in the organisation or by government;
- new legislation;
- changes in funding levels.

Examples of internal forces include:

- new team members;
- development of a revised team philosophy;
- a change of team leader.

When change is constant and imposed, staff can become demoralised and stressed. Remain aware of local and national developments and try to anticipate their likely impact on the work of your team. When possible, you should take positive action to prepare the team and so help staff to exert some degree of control over events. For instance:

- The Government normally announces new legislation well in advance. Make sure you obtain relevant documents for the team; arrange in-house sessions to discuss the changes and their implications; and consider ways in which you may have to change working practices to meet new requirements.
- Many organisations are emphasising individual accountability; this is often reinforced by systems such as staff appraisal. If you don't yet have a formal system in place, you can prepare by introducing some components of appraisal. These might include carrying out annual staff development discussions with each member of the team.

11.3 Real or apparent change?

Change is always open to interpretation. Often, it is hard to tell whether any real change has taken place at all! Sometimes people who feel under threat will create the impression of change to satisfy the boss. This is possible because people at different levels in the organisation perceive change in different ways and will use different methods to assess whether change has occurred.

Senior management, for example, may rely on documentary evidence, such as reassuring reports written by middle managers. Nearer the 'shop floor', however, little may have altered. Before you accept change as genuine, make sure you have valid evidence.

ACTIVITY

A community nursing service has decided to introduce a systematic approach to quality improvement. Senior management has told all management staff that they 'must do something about quality'. However, little or no training has taken place. Most managers, being professional nurses, have heard of the 'standard setting' approach from their professional journals. They decide to try this out.

Each team writes a number of standards to cover important areas of its work. These standards are forwarded to senior management which replies with a congratulatory memorandum. Little more is heard from senior management.

- Is this a satisfactory state of affairs?
- If not, why not?
- How would you have done things differently, (a) as a supervisory manager in this situation and (b) as one of the senior managers?

11.4 Facilitating change

There are many ways in which you can help to make change a manageable experience.

Show a positive yet realistic attitude

Try to model an attitude which conveys how change can be a positive opportunity. However, avoid coming across as a change evangelist. Be prepared to share your own worries and reservations but show how you try to cope with these.

Be proactive

Don't wait around for change to hit you; try to predict where change is likely to be needed and suggest your own solutions. Do this in conjunction with your team so that they see how a positive attitude can work in practice. Using the power of the team and its views in this way will help to maintain energy and morale.

Divide changes into manageable chunks

This helps to avoid staff feeling overwhelmed by the onset of huge changes. All managers have a duty to negotiate strongly with senior management about the degree of change which their team can handle in any given time period.

Involve your staff

Respect your staff by keeping them involved and informed. Don't be persuaded by those who argue that change has to be driven through regardless of the consequences to people.

Get outside help

Occasionally, you might find it valuable to employ an outside person to help with easing in change. This person could be someone from elsewhere in the organisation, or might be an external consultant.

In many situations, the simplest solutions are often very effective. One way of dispelling fears and anxieties is to invite someone who has already been through a similar process of change. Another is to arrange a visit to an organisation where change has occurred. It is often quite startling how these experiences can change the approach of individual team members. Working in one organisation can encourage a blinkered view of the world – it becomes difficult to imagine alternatives. Just seeing how someone else has done it can be enough in itself to create the conditions for change at home.

ACTIVITY

Consider the pros and cons of internal and external consultants in helping to facilitate change. What are your conclusions? There are many variables that you should take into account, including objectivity, knowledge, trust, confidentiality and cost.

ACTIVITY

1 Select an area of your work which involves significant change and which is giving you some problems. Think about the following questions:
- Do you know of someone else who has been through the same experience? If not, who could you ask who might know?
- Are there other organisations, sufficiently similar to your own, that you could arrange to visit? Again, if not, who could tell you?
- How much would it cost the department/unit/team to make selected visits?

2 Reading your professional journals should give you many ideas – contact names, organisations, innovations to investigate and so on. Write to authors of articles and books about their experiences. In the main they will be only too willing to reply. If an article describes an organisational innovation, most places will be willing to accept visitors; a phone call will let you decide. Get in early, though, before the queue starts! A practical tip is to look through the journals which are a year or two old. The authors of articles will probably have experienced the initial flush of enthusiasm from the readers and will be able to fit in your queries more easily. The change itself will also have had a longer time to mature.

11.5 Personal consequences of change

Change is challenging and it can also be enjoyable. However, a positive outcome cannot be guaranteed by any means and you should be aware of the negative consequences of introducing change.

ACTIVITY

'Not another bloody meeting'

Mary Staples had been promoted recently to supervisor within her own place of work – 'Levetts', a residential home for older people. She was full of her new responsibilities and spent many hours at home planning how she was going to improve client care. Jokingly, her husband called her 'Miss Levetts' because of her obvious commitment to the home and the clients. She had enormous difficulty 'switching off' at the end of a shift. She would often stay late at work attending quality assurance meetings. When she went home, she took with her a briefcase bulging with papers. After a time, her husband began to react with some irritation. Prior to her promotion, they had been able to go out together twice a week; now they were lucky to get out once a month.

- Do you recognise this situation?
- Is this a problem or is it just a case of a couple having to adapt to changing circumstances?
- If you were a work colleague, what advice would you give Mary?

Learning from failures

Change places new demands on us and failure is commonplace and often inevitable. However, we often neglect to learn from these experiences because most of us are brought up to strive for success. Too often we see failure as unacceptable and something to be hidden at all costs. The paradox is that we must learn to accept some failures in order to achieve new solutions and to innovate.

What can we learn from our failures? Our failures can:

- promote reflection;
- stimulate change;
- provide useful information which may not have surfaced without this 'failure';
- give feedback on our actions;
- encourage flexibility;
- teach humility;
- increase determination;
- improve our tolerance to frustration in the future;
- promote experimentation.

Try to create a work atmosphere in which staff are prepared to take reasonable risks and to acknowledge their failures as well as their successes. Care work is centred on human relationships and these are impossible to 'get right' all the time. This being the case, care workers will often feel that they could have done better. Referring back to Chapter 3, you will see that this is a necessary aspect of being a reflective practitioner.

Burn-out

Burn-out affects many people but it seems to be especially common amongst carers. Prolonged and intense contact with other people appears to be one of the contributory factors. One definition of burn-out is:

> *A state of physical and emotional exhaustion which brings about a lowering of self-esteem and a lack of interest in the job and the clients.*

It makes interpersonal relationships much less satisfying, whether these are in or outside of work.

What makes burn-out more likely? Factors include:

- unrelenting stress and dissatisfaction;
- poor relationships outside work;
- few chances to relax and unwind with others;
- loneliness;
- painful life events, such as divorce, bereavement or illness;
- unrealistically high self-expectations;
- an authoritarian style of leadership;
- an inability to delegate;
- a job in which responsibilities are very unclear, where the job-holder has too many roles to perform;
- powerlessness – 'whatever I do, nothing changes';
- social attitudes which may aggravate the situation, for example unrealistically high expectations that many people have of care workers.

If you recognise these factors in any of your staff, you should consider carefully how you can help. If you recognise them in yourself, you will have to decide whether you are able to manage the problem yourself or whether you should seek outside help, perhaps from an independent counsellor.

How can you recognise burn-out? There are many possible features, as shown in the box below.

RECOGNISING BURN-OUT

Psychological:

Intolerance and irritability	Feelings of guilt
Rigid, inflexible attitudes	Loneliness
Boredom and cynicism	Feelings of helplessness
Depression	Less pleasure from relationships

Physical:

Tiredness and exhaustion	High blood pressure
Sleep problems	Low back pain and headaches

Behaviour changes:

Worsening performance at work	Excessive alcohol intake
Accident proneness	Drug abuse

From time to time, everyone will experience one or other of the features of burn-out. This is normal. However, if you feel that a member of your team is looking particularly stressed or 'worn-out', be prepared to act. Action might be as little as making a point to have coffee with the person concerned to give them the chance to talk. If this simple approach doesn't work, or seems inappropriate, decide whether you feel you can handle the situation yourself in the first instance or whether you should refer the person to someone more appropriately qualified. If you are undecided, talk it over with your own manager, the personnel department or another person whose views you trust and respect. Make sure you know how to refer someone for further help if necessary.

Preventing and managing burn-out

In your management role, you have considerable responsibility for preventing and managing burn-out and stress both in yourself and in members of your team. There are several approaches:

Education

All staff need to understand the nature of stress and burn-out: their causes, effects, prevention and management. Because of the values of the care sector, caring for staff should be given a very high priority indeed. There is also a duty on the part of the employer to ensure that all staff are made aware of the risks inherent in their work; and a responsibility on the part of employees to do all they can to prevent problems. Build this process of education into the everyday work of the team. Show that you are aware of work stresses by advising and supporting staff to minimise these.

Self-care

Care can be both physically and emotionally demanding. It is important for all care workers to look after themselves. Health promotion advice is widely available – in magazines and newspapers, on TV and radio, occupational health departments, doctors' surgeries and from health education units. Chronic physical disability, such as back pain, can produce severe psychological consequences such as depression, and so there is every reason to try to keep fit.

At a more personal level, staff should to monitor their 'distance' from clients' circumstances and problems. Different roles demand different boundaries, of course. The key is to recognise when relationships are becoming too demanding. In areas of work where professional supervision is offered, this will be the most appropriate forum for discussing these sensitive issues.

> **ACTIVITY**
>
> Over a period of one week, focus your attention on the impact that current working patterns are having on team members. In the course of this, consider the following questions:
>
> - Is the balance of workload distributed fairly across the team?
> - Are you putting too much stress on inexperienced staff, even though they might be very keen?
> - Are the roles within the team sufficiently clear or do you get problems of overlap, confusion and conflict?
> - Are you overdependent on the 'willing horse' in the team? Do you find it easier to ask the person you know will agree than to ask the person most suited?

Social involvement

An active social life outside work is very helpful in protecting against the worst consequences of stress and burn-out. There are no simple or easy answers here and everyone has different needs in this respect. Do take note, however, if any of your staff are becoming unusually isolated and withdrawn.

Reducing work-related stress

This is part of your overall task, demonstrated through the ways in which you organise tasks or discuss plans and negotiate roles within the team. However, you should also review the nature of the work solely from the point of view of its stress potential.

11.6 Learning to enjoy change

In work situations where change is continuous, survival depends on your ability to adapt successfully. The first step is to abandon any expectation that things can revert to an earlier 'golden age' of complete stability. Remember that change can give new opportunities for staff who have creative and innovative ideas.

As we have seen earlier, there is little doubt that some people adjust better to these conditions than others. But that is the case whatever the prevailing system. However, everyone needs some degree of security and stability in which to work and to give of their best. You have an especially difficult task as a manager because you have to search for ways to meet two apparently conflicting demands. These are:

1 The need to encourage staff to accept, adapt to, and even welcome change;
2 The need to create sufficient stability to allow effective work to take place.

Try to produce a situation where each person has a realistic and balanced mixture of job demands: some which are relatively stable – to provide continuity – and others that are more fluid and allow individuals to express their creativity. You will soon find that an equal balance does not usually work: staff tend to prefer one or the other end of the spectrum. Your job is to recognise who likes what!

Create conditions in which all staff become gradually accustomed to increasing change and flexibility. Provide adequate but not overwhelming information about changes in the organisation. This could be through staff meetings, newsletters, informal memos or noticeboards.

When you want a new development to go well, involve someone who is likely to succeed. This is not as obvious as it sounds. Some organisations operate very bureaucratically and react to new demands in a rigid,

ACTIVITY

Harry Fenton, the manager of a day care service for physically handicapped people, is asked to give a talk to a local residents' association about what care is on offer. This is seen as a high status activity and so Harry decides that he must do it himself because 'no-one else really understands the details'. The talk is a disaster because Harry – although generally a very effective manager – is certainly no public speaker and cannot adjust to the level of his audience. His talk is full of social service jargon and the audience is left bewildered. Sue, Harry's deputy, is much better suited to this kind of role. She has not worked in the service for as long but finds it very easy to establish a quick rapport with groups of strangers – never Harry's strong point – and talks in a down-to-earth way. Had Harry noticed this and spent a little time briefing Sue on those areas with which she was less familiar, the talk could have been a success. Moreover, Sue would have gained valuable experience and Harry would have enhanced his reputation as a good manager, able to recognise and exploit the strengths of his staff.

- Have you come across situations like the one described above?
- How would you go about choosing the right person for this kind of task?

status-bound way. A certain task may go to someone because of position rather than skills. The new idea may well fail, not because it was bad in itself but because the wrong person was chosen to implement it.

Tom Peters, in his book entitled *Thriving on Chaos*, said that managers at all levels need to challenge conventional wisdom and learn to tackle new problems in new ways. His ideas on this topic are worth considering:

Be creative:

- Think flexibly and laterally, in other words don't assume that what has worked in the past will work again; be prepared to 'think the unthinkable'.

Provide direction:

- Develop a vision which will inspire others;
- Manage by example;
- Get out and about – don't supervise from the office.

Empower staff:

- Listen to colleagues;
- Take what they say very seriously indeed;
- Delegate real responsibility.

Challenge bureaucracy

- Encourage communication across organisational boundaries, for example by getting your staff into other departments to learn about systems which will help your area in the long run. Don't be put off by the comment 'that hasn't been done before'; it may mean that you have come up with a very good idea indeed!

If you take these thoughts as a basis for your own philosophy of supervisory management, and strive to develop the powers of reflective practice, you'll be well on your way to becoming an effective and caring manager.

Reading on ...

★ de Bono, Edward (1990) *The Use of Lateral Thinking*, Penguin, London. Edward de Bono has written extensively on the topic of creativity and lateral thinking.

★ Payne, Roy and Firth Cozens, Jenny (eds) (1987) *Stress in Health Professionals*, John Wiley and Sons, Chichester. This book describes the stresses involved in the work of a wide range of health and social care professionals. Occupations include social workers, nurses, GPs and dentists.

★ Peters, Tom (1989) *Thriving on Chaos*, Pan Books, London. This is full of interest. Not a book to be read from cover to cover but well worth while dipping into when you need to refresh your thinking on management.

Appendix 1: How to find out more

NVQ/SVQs and other vocational qualifications

There are well over 100 bodies awarding NVQs across the whole range of occupations. Only some of these will be relevant to the care sector but remember to look at more than just the care or management NVQ/SVQs if you have responsibility for a range of staff, such as cooks and secretaries. The majority of relevant awarding bodies are listed here but, if you need to find out about the full range of available NVQ/SVQs, contact the National Council for Vocational Qualifications (NCVQ). SCOTVEC will be able to give you details about the situation in Scotland.

If you are a qualified health or social care professional, you can find out more about relevant qualifications from your own professional body or statutory council.

Business and Technology Education Council (BTEC)
Central House
Upper Woburn Place
London WC1H 0HH

Tel. 0171 413 8400
Fax 0171 387 6068

Central Council for Education and Training in Social Work (CCETSW)
Derbyshire House
St Chad's Street
London WC1 8AD

Tel. 0171 278 2455
Fax 0171 278 2934

City & Guilds of London Institute (C&G)
1 Giltspur Street
London EC1A 9DD

Tel. 0171 294 2468
Fax 0171 294 2400

Council for Awards in Children's Care and Education (CACHE)
8 Chequer Street
St Albans AL1 3XZ

Tel. 01727 847636
Fax 01727 867609

Institute of Management
Management House
Cottingham Road
Corby
Northants NN17 1TT

Tel. 01536 204222
Fax 01536 201651

Institute of Supervisory Management
Mansell House
22 Bore Street
Lichfield
Staffordshire WS13 6LP

Tel. 01543 251346
Fax 01543 415804

Institute of Training and Development
Institute Road
Marlow
Buckinghamshire SL7 1BN

Tel. 01628 890123
Fax 01628 890208

Local Government Management Board
Arndale House
The Arndale Centre
Luton LU1 2TS

Tel. 01582 451166
Fax 01582 412525

Management Charter Initiative (MCI)
Russell Square House
10–12 Russell Square
London WC1B 5BZ

Tel. 0171 872 9000
Fax 0171 872 9099

National Examinations Board for Supervision and Management (NEBS Management)
1 Giltspur Street
London EC1A 9DD

Tel. 0171 294 2470
Fax 0171 294 2402

RSA Examining Board (RSA)
Progress House
Westwood Way
Coventry

Tel. 01203 470033
Fax 01203 468080

SCOTVEC
Hanover House
24 Douglas Street
Glasgow G2 7NQ

Tel. 0141 248 7900
Fax 0141 242 2244

Educational materials

You or your staff may wish to study for a qualification by distance learning. You can obtain information about suitable courses and training materials from:

Local Government Management Board
Address as above

National Extension College
18 Brooklands Avenue
Cambridge CB2 2HN

Tel. 01223 316644
Fax 01223 313586

The Open University
Walton Hall
Milton Keynes MK7 6YY

Tel. 01908 653473
Fax 01908 654320

The Open College
St Paul's
781 Wilmslow Road
Didsbury
Manchester M20 8RW

Tel. 0161 434 0007
Fax 0161 434 1061

Appendix 2: The MCI Standards

This book provides the underpinning knowledge you need to develop your skills and understanding of supervisory management whatever your role or qualifications. You may also wish to register for NVQ/SVQs and so gain formal recognition of your supervisory management competence through this route.

Like all occupational standards, the Management Standards are reviewed and revised at regular intervals. Management Charter Initiative (MCI), the lead body, consults managers and others across a wide range of industries with the aim of producing a set of standards which reflects current good practice.

At present, the MCI Supervisory Management Standards consist of seven units. The NHS Training Directorate has adapted these so that they are more suitable for use in the health care sector. The units are grouped around four key roles: manage services; manage finance; manage people; manage information.

Each unit consists of elements of competence which are themselves made up of performance criteria (PCs). To gain a National Vocational Qualification, candidates have to demonstrate competence in all the PCs in a variety of circumstances (these are described in the range statements linked to each element).

The following table shows the main links between the key roles, units, and the contents of this book.

Key role		**Chapter**
Manage services	Unit 1 Maintain services and systems to meet quality standards	7
Manage finance	Unit 2 Contribute to the planning, monitoring and control of resources	8
Manage people	Unit 3 Contribute to the provision of personnel	9
	Unit 4 Contribute to the training and development of teams, individuals and self to enhance performance	10
	Unit 5 Contribute to the planning, organisation and evaluation of work	6
	Unit 6 Create, maintain and enhance productive working relationships	4
Manage information	Unit 7 Provide information and advice for action towards meeting organisational objectives	5

Several priorities have emerged during the latest review of the Standards (on-going at the time of writing). These priorities include the following topics which are covered in this book. You will immediately recognise that each of these topics is of great concern to staff working in health and social care. The revised Standards are likely to retain the key roles outlined above (perhaps with minor changes in terminology).

The links with the contents of this book are as follows.

Environmental considerations	Dealt with specifically in section 8.4
Equal opportunities	Applies throughout the book, with specific references in sections 4.5 and 9.3
Ethical considerations and values	Values are central to the whole book, but you will find specific references in Chapters 1, 2 and in section 3.2
Quality issues	Covered in detail in Chapter 7
Personal competence and development	Most of this book is about how you can develop your personal competence as a supervisory manager. You will find references to specific aspects in sections 2.4, 2.5, 3.3, 4.3, 4.4, 5.1, 6.3, 10.8, 11.6
Team focus	The main references are in Chapter 4

The contents of Chapters 2, 3 and 11 apply across all the units, as they deal with the context within which supervisory management takes place. Only the main text links have been shown in the table: management is an integrated activity which, in practice, cannot be broken down into small isolated components. When faced with a real work situation, try to use the book in an integrated way, picking out information from various chapters to suit your needs.

Bibliography

de Bono, Edward 1990. *The Use of Lateral Thinking*. London: Penguin.

British Journal of Healthcare Computing – this provides up-to-date news and articles about all aspects of computing in health care.

Buzan, Tony 1995. *Use Your Head*. London: BBC Publications.

Cassam, Emlyn and Gupta, Hima 1992. *Quality assurance for social care agencies*. Harlow: Longman Group UK Ltd.

Catt, Stephen E. and Miller, Donald S. 1991. *Supervision: working with people*. Boston: Irwin.

Community Care Series on Purchasing: 28 October 1993 to 16/23 December 1993 (No. 990 to 997).

Connor, Anne and Black, Stewart (eds) 1994. *Performance Review and Quality in Social Care*. London: Jessica Kingsley Publishers.

Crosby, Philip B. 1993. *Quality is Free*. Signet. (Distributed by Penguin Books Ltd., Harmondsworth).

Department of Trade and Industry 1990. *The Case for Quality*. DTI Enterprise Initiative.

Donabedian, Avedis 1986. Criteria and standards for quality assessment and monitoring. *QRB*, **12**, March 1986.

Douglas, Robin and Payne, Chris 1988. *Organising for learning*. National Institute for Social Work.

Ewles, Linda and Simnett, Ina 1992. *Promoting health: A practical guide*. London: Scutari Press.

Gowers, Sir Ernest 1987. *The Complete Plain Words*. Harmondsworth: Penguin (Revised by Sidney Greenbaum and Janet Whitcut).

Handy, Charles B. 1993. *Understanding Organisations*. Penguin Books.

Handy, Charles 1990. *Inside Organisations: 21 ideas for managers*. London: BBC Books.

Hargie, Owen (ed.) 1988. *A Handbook of Communication Skills*. London: Routledge.

Janis, Irving 1971. Groupthink, *Psychology Today*, 5, November 1971, pp. 43–46, 74–76.

Jones, Rowan, and Pendlebury, Maurice 1992. *Public Sector Accounting*. London: Pitman Publishing Inc.

Kitson, Alison 1987. Raising standards of clinical practice – the fundamental issues of effective nursing practice. *Journal of Advanced Nursing*, **12**, pp. 321–329.

Maxwell, Robert 1984. Quality assessment in health. *British Medical Journal*, **288**, 12 May 1984, pp. 1470–1472.

Mayeroff, Milton 1990. *On Caring*. New York: Harper Perennial.

National Care Homes Association 1993. *Health and Safety in a Caring Environment*.

Øvretveit, John 1992. *Health Service Quality: An Introduction to Quality Methods for Health Services*. London: Blackwell Scientific Publications.

Oxford Dictionary of English Grammar 1993. Oxford University Press.

Oxford Guide to English Usage 1993. Oxford University Press.

Parsley, Karen and Corrigan, Philomena 1994. *Quality Improvement in Nursing and Healthcare*. London: Chapman and Hall.

Payne, Roy and Firth-Cozens, Jenny 1987. *Stress in Health Professionals*. Chichester: John Wiley and Sons.

Penguin Dictionary of English Synonyms and Antonyms 1992. Harmondsworth: Penguin.

Peters, Tom 1989. *Thriving on Chaos*. London: Macmillan.

Robson, Mike 1988. *Quality Circles - A Practical Guide*. Aldershot: Gower.

Rogers, Jenny 1989. *Adults Learning*. Milton Keynes: Open University Press.

Roget's Thesaurus (latest edition). Harlow: Longman.

Schön, Donald A. 1991. *The Reflective Practitioner*. Aldershot: Avebury.

Shaw, Charles 1986. *Introducing Quality Assurance*. King Edward's Hospital Fund for London.

Stark, Michael 1991. *Not for profit, not for sale*. Policy Journals in Association with the Chartered Institute of Management Accountants.

Tuckman, B. 1973. in Napier, Rodney W. and Gerfhenfeld, Matti K. (eds) *Group Theory and Experience*. Boston: Houghton Mifflin.

Venolia, Janet G. 1991. *Write Right*. Nairn: David St John Thomas Publisher.

World Health Organisation 1984. *Health Promotion: a WHO Discussion Document on the Concepts and Principles*.

Index